the 13 secrets of sexual control

by
Robert Denryck

Carnell Ltd.

THE 13 SECRETS OF SEXUAL CONTROL
by Robert Denryck

Published in Great Britain MCMXCVI by Carnell Ltd,
28 Charles Square, London N1 6HT

Typeset by Typesetting Solutions, Slough, Berks.

Printed by Clays Ltd, St Ives plc.

ISBN 1-85779-992-5

This book is dedicated to everyone seeking . . .
Intensely shared pleasure
Infinite sensuality
A new definition of virility
True loving harmony . . .

The Publisher

Contents

Introduction

"The longer the battle rages, the better warrior he becomes, and greater grows his courage. His companion's Deep Valley is no longer a bottomless abyss. He makes proper contact with its sides and down to its depths. His companion's body starts trembling and shivering with delight; cries of pleasure escape her lips. The grass and bushes around her Deep Valley are inundated with the dew of ecstasy. He pretends to look for a cloth to clean away her juices, but she stops him. The battle of love, she thinks, should be one of savage frenzy, like the ecstatic temple dances accompanied by gongs and drums."

Jou Pu Tan

As this marvellous ancient Chinese text demonstrates, Taoists elevated sexuality to the stature of a veritable art. It held a sacred significance for them, and was never taken lightly, or relegated to the level of a simple, often clumsy, biological function. Taoist lovers –

already well ahead of the popular beliefs of their own time – considered women as their equals, with full rights to the highest degree of sexual fulfilment. They even discovered that women's faculties for pleasure was greater than their own, if only they could learn how to release it.

Can twentieth-century lovers, strengthened – or should we say weakened – by nineteen centuries of progress, claim as much today? Is our modern battle of love one of savage frenzy, like an ecstatic dance? Can we make our companion's body – and heart – tremble and shiver with delight?

In truth, if we were to chronicle the progress of modern sensuality, we would have to concentrate more on its failures than its achievements. How is it that so little progress has been made over the millennia? How is it possible that we seem to have actually regressed, as far as sexual practices and attitudes are concerned, or, if not actually regressed, then certainly slowed down? Who is at fault? Why is it that, despite the best intentions of lovers, sexual dissatisfaction is the norm in modern society?

Without meaning to offend any phallocrats or disciples of machismo, we believe the problem often lies with men. The majority of men, if they were honest, would agree. And they would be hard put to find any women who would contradict this statement. Most women feel they are not being made love to the way they should – and rightly so.

Balzac said it with great humility and precision:

"There are no frigid women, only unskilled men."

Without knowing it, Balzac was repeating one of the premises of ancient Chinese wisdom.

Taoists have been aware of the formidable erotic power of women for centuries, and have identified the weak link in the erotic chain as men's inability to remain at the height of pleasure or to retain their sensual explosion. In other words, Taoists understood that one of the essential prerequisites for a couple's pleasure is that the man not let his partner down at precisely the moment when she is in most need of his intimate constancy.

However, despite their pretensions, men frequently lack this ability. The consequence of this is so depressing to women that they sometimes lose interest in celebrating the joys of love at all.

Taoism being a practical philosophy, its sages were not content to simply identify the problem. They also suggested some astonishingly simple, yet effective remedies. Remedies that anyone can apply, without any excessive effort, and which, in most cases, are being discovered – or actually rediscovered – by modern medical science.

This short treatise is the fruit of long hours of research, and provides a concise guide to these ancient Taoist practices. It reveals little-known secrets of the art of loving, and demonstrates how they should be applied (both by couples and single persons).

The Taoist art of loving intensifies sexual ecstasy to heights of pleasure most people would not have imagined possible. It helps men remain virile well into old age, which is of extreme benefit to couples, since women's desires do not diminish with age as dramatically as men's. The art of loving is also one of the keys to longevity, which is closely linked to sexual energy and vitality.

This book will initiate you into the secrets of the ancient Taoist masters. It is of special interest to:

- Couples who find their sex life routine, and who would like to explore new dimensions of sexuality and love.

- People who have serious sexual problems and who are looking for effective solutions (especially if so-called traditional therapeutic methods have failed).

- Men who want to learn how to preserve their virility well into old age.

- Men and women who are looking for a way to harmonise spirituality and sexuality.

- Single persons who want to know how to stay in shape between partners, or who need to channel their sexual energy (libido) so that it does not become a problem.

- Middle-aged men who wish to increase their vitality and mental clarity, and who want to remain sexually active as they grow older.

- And, of course, women who would like their partners to exhibit more enthusiasm and endurance.

As you will see throughout this book, the optimum functioning of the sexual organs depends on a variety of factors. This is why some of the techniques described are designed for the entire body, while others concern the genital areas alone. In many cases, you will obtain immediate results by applying one or another of the secret Taoist techniques. But it is certainly preferable to practice all the exercises, so that the results you obtain become more profound and lasting.

And, in fact, the aim of this book is to lead you from simple genital pleasure to a level of ecstasy that will inundate your entire body and being.

A short initiation into the philosophy of the ancient Taoists

Five hundred years before the Christian era, Lao Tsu attained the wisdom of Tao. To the ancient Chinese, the word Tao meant the Great Totality – the unfathomable mystery of Nature, the infinite energy of life.

The origin of Taoism lies in this experience of Lao Tsu. We know almost nothing about this venerable sage. However, he did leave us with a very short, very concise guide – the *Tao Te King*. Other remarkable masters like Lie Tseu and Tchouang Tseu carried on the tradition of Tao. The greatest intellectuals of ancient China used it to develop an art of living. Doctors were inspired by it in their efforts to promote health, sexual prowess and longevity. Thanks to Taoism, people were able to reach a very old age, while remaining in full possession of their mental and physical abilities. They also attained a remarkable balance between spirituality and sensuality.

The aim of every Taoist is to live in the spirit of Tao. They therefore favour what is natural over everything that is artificial and restrictive, whether in the form of absurd laws, narrow-minded morals, or simple injustice.

AN AMAZING TEACHING

Taoism will certainly surprise people who were brought up in the Judeo-Christian tradition. In fact, its most important commandment is to be relaxed, and to remain faithful to your own nature. Wisdom means being able to accept yourself the way you are. It's useless to try and be something special – all you have to do is be yourself.

Why sacrifice or torture yourself? Renouncing earthly pleasures does not bring us any closer to heaven. It would be better to respect nature and cultivate our love of life.

Sexuality is an integral part of human happiness; it should not be restricted by taboos and fears based on ignorance and superstition. Taoists consider coitus to be the most accessible means of experiencing the Sacred (whatever name you give it). For them, eroticism and mysticism are indissoluble. Tao becomes manifest with the separation (of matter) into Yin and Yang. During coitus, we can reunite the Yin and Yang energies, and return to the state of Tao, which is the origin of all things.

TAOIST TREATISES ON LOVE

Ancient China had its own sex manuals – Taoist treatises on the art of loving. But their tone was different from that of most modern works on the subject. Science and technology, of course, were much less developed at the time, and were replaced by a dimension of poetic expression, whose beauty can be admired even today.

Human sexuality is not just a question of organs and genital performance. The sexual act is far from being purely mechanical. It represents a total experience. Sexology is not just a science, but also an art. Lovers must make use of all their senses and imagination to attain the true state of harmony resulting from the union of Yin and Yang.

So the Taoist treatises on love are written in a rather flowery, poetic style, instead of in the clinical tone we are accustomed to in our own manuals. The erect penis is referred to as the Jade Peak; the vagina as the Deep Valley. This adds an element of charm to the Taoist texts which, although written centuries ago, still have so much to teach us.

FROM ORDINARY ORGASM TO TAOIST ORGASM

Through its extraordinary techniques of sexual control, Taoism will lead you to new heights of pleasure. In fact, the aim of Taoist eroticism is not the attainment of sexual pleasure as we know it, but of total ecstasy. It has, therefore, developed techniques for exploring and utilising the complete potential of human sexual energy. In comparison, our own erotic methods are still in the Dark Ages.

To better understand the difference between ordinary orgasm and Taoist orgasm, we will make a little detour, and first discuss the biology of the human brain.

YOUR REAL SEX ORGAN
IS YOUR BRAIN

Modern research has confirmed the fact that the centre of orgasm lies in the brain. The penis is only one erogenous zone among a number of others. As the American Doctor R. Heath showed in 1972, powerful orgasms can be produced solely by stimulating the septum, which is the core of the body's limbic system. The septum, therefore, represents the primary orgasm centre in the brain.

In his experiments, Dr. Heath produced orgasms in women by injecting acetylcholine into their septum. Other experiments have shown how electrical stimulation can produce orgasm, both in animals and in humans. Consuming certain drugs, like the infamous crack, can also produce actual orgasms. In the US people have been experimenting with a number of devices which are reputed to induce states of ecstasy. These devices modify brainwaves, and stimulate certain areas of the brain using light and sound.

The most recent research seems to point to the importance of neurotransmitters, like acetylcholine, endorphins, serotonin and dopamine, on our pleasure centres. Neurotransmitters are hormones which facilitate the transmission of nervous impulses from neuron to neuron, and which play a part in all experiences of pleasure, whether produced by drugs, sex, or any other pleasant activity.

Another important point: the mechanism of ejaculation is linked to a cerebral centre which is different from that which controls orgasm. Men are, therefore, perfectly capable of experiencing an orgasm without ejaculating, and also . . . of ejaculating without having an orgasm!

As you will see, these modern discoveries are extremely important in gaining a full understanding of the Taoist art of loving.

EXPLOSIVE AND IMPLOSIVE ORGASMS

Taoists found a way to stimulate the brain's pleasure to well above normal levels. This method is the retention of the ejaculatory spasm, which in turn creates a powerful accumulation of sexual energy. When people acquire an increased level of sexual energy, they can channel it to regions in the brain which are usually not stimulated. This technique of storing and channelling sexual energy leads to another type of orgasm, which is termed implosive orgasm, and which represents a very different experience from that of ordinary, explosive orgasm.

EXPLOSIVE ORGASM

This is the classical type of orgasm described by Masters and Johnson. In graphic terms, a curve, representing pleasure, ascends more or less rapidly, until orgasm accompanied by ejaculation is achieved. The orgasm is followed by an extremely rapid descent of the curve. The state of exhaustion or apathy following orgasm corresponds to a diminished level of energy, which is often so severe that men fall asleep. This kind of orgasm is generally regarded as an expenditure – and therefore a loss – of energy.

Traditional orgasm results in a violent discharge of psycho-genital tension. The experience, although very pleasant, is also very brief.

IMPLOSIVE ORGASM

Taoists also call this form 'valley orgasm'. Although little known in the west, some sexologists have reported its existence. In this type of orgasm, ejaculation does not play a major role. If it does occur at all, it can take place after a number of orgasms. And in fact, contrary to popular belief, men do have the potential to be multi-orgasmic. The key to this type of experience resides in being able to approach the point of no return, that is to say, when ejaculation becomes inevitable, without going past it.

The idea of orgasm without ejaculation may sound like something out of a science fiction novel to those who take it for granted that the equation 'orgasm = ejaculation' is valid. However, modern technology has confirmed what the ancient Taoists knew intuitively. Kinsey, for example, in his work *Sexual Behaviour in Men,* states that:

> "Orgasm may take place without any emission of sperm. [...] Certain adult males experience orgasm [...] by contracting their genital muscles, as they practice the contraceptive technique known as coitus reservatus. These individuals experience real orgasm, which they can easily identify, without ejaculation taking place."

In Taoist orgasm, the spasm is produced in a very different way. In fact, the experience of pleasure in Taoism is more like reaching a plateau of prolonged ecstasy than tumbling over a summit and ejaculating. The pleasure spasms are felt throughout the body, and this diffusion of sexual energy produces a range of experiences which are much more varied than those felt during ordinary sexual relations.

Sometimes the charge of sexual energy localised in the genital organs is transformed into a current of intense heat, which radiates throughout the body. Sometimes, sexual excitation is perceived as a cascade of smooth, cooling energy, which seems to spurt from the head, down through the rest of the body. The energy can also start in the feet, and move from one part of the body to another like a ray of fire. In all cases, your neuromuscular system relaxes completely, and orgasm is never followed by fatigue or lassitude. You feel recharged by a powerful current of vital energy and love.

On one level, you experience a state of fusion and voluptuous communion with your partner. In some instances, you may get the strange feeling that you are literally inside your partner's body and mind, or you may feel her entering you.

This feeling of fusion can also extend to everything you perceive. The colours in the room, the singing of birds in the garden, the immensity of the night sky through the window, the cries of children in the street – all seem to form an elevated and mysterious reality which encompasses both your partner and yourself.

You are everything, and everything is you. You perceive the same reality as usual, but it suddenly seems amazingly coherent and peaceful. Objects have an unaccustomed transparency and lightness. In short, you rediscover the magic of the world, which the stress of day-to-day life usually obscures with a veil of banality or boredom.

In addition to this newfound source of energy, you may experience psychological insights which are very special. Solutions to problems which have been bothering you for a long time suddenly surge from your mind. These solutions may even take the form of precise visions, which fill you with feelings of certainty and tranquillity.

THE GATELESS GATE

Of course, these kinds of things won't happen without some work on your self. In the process of Taoist transformation, the Old Man must die in order to be replaced by the New Man. Perseverance and discipline are required. But the Taoist view of effort is quite different from our own crude, muscular approach.

Work on the self means, above all, maintaining a state of vigilance and lucidity, and has nothing to do with following some kind of forced programme designed to make you attain a spiritual or intellectual ideal. In Taoism, making a violent effort to resolve your problems is a little like trying to break down a door that is already open. The mind often imagines the worst, and creates obstacles where, in fact, there are none. It is the mind which creates the walls of an imaginary prison all around us, limiting our potential and our development.

The gateway that leads to the realisation of Tao is already wide open. It is a gateless gate. "When your mind has no limits, your happiness will have no limits," said one Chinese sage. Behind the apparent horrors and contradictions of this world lies a hidden world of light and harmony. But unlike Christianity, which claims that paradise exists in another world entirely, Taoism affirms that our own world can become a place of permanent ecstasy, right here and now.

It is through the Deep Valley (the vagina) that we all entered this world of material illusions and suffering. According to Taoist philosophy, you have to go back through the Deep Valley to escape the prison of the five senses. If you give pleasure, and attain the state of ecstasy yourself, the Guardian of the Deep Valley will accept you and allow you to leave. She becomes the Great Liberator who will initiate you into the mysteries of Tao and the Supreme Reality.

In Taoism, this is a question of becoming perfectly familiar with the five senses through experimentation, so that they stop deceiving and tormenting you. This is far from the Christian ethic developed in the Middle Ages, which claims that the vagina is the gateway to hell! Taoism, on the contrary, considers the Jade Door to be the gateway to the Secret Temple, where the great mysteries of life and death are revealed. The ancient Taoists developed remarkably effective techniques for attaining this knowledge. These techniques could be used to open this Gateless Gate, which leads to the realisation of Tao, and perfect male-female union.

Without further ado then, here are the thirteen keys which will allow you to open the Gateless Gate.

The First Secret

———— ◆ ————

Boiling the
water of Yin

THE IMPORTANCE OF
THE FEMALE ORGASM

The anatomical structures which produce the sensation of orgasm are very similar in men and women. But the resulting experiences are quite different. About 10 to 15 per cent of women can have a number of successive orgasms, without the recuperation period required by men between ejaculations. And even when women have only a single orgasm, the rhythmic contractions that characterise their climaxes can last much longer than those of men.

In Greek mythology, we find the astonishing account of a man who changed sexes.

One day, while walking on a lonely path, young Tiresias encountered two snakes, interlaced in loving embrace, at his feet. While they were thus absorbed, Tiresias seized the opportunity to beat them to death with his walking-stick. As a punishment for this act, he was immediately transformed into a woman.

At first incredulous, he was soon forced to accept the reality of his condition, and adapt to a new life in a woman's body. Years later, when he once again encountered a pair of interlaced snakes, he took great care not to disturb them. As a reward, the punishment was lifted, and he regained his masculine form.

It then happened that Zeus, King of the gods, engaged in a discussion with his wife Hera on the subject of pleasure in men and women. Which of the two sexes gained the most satisfaction from coitus?

Zeus and Hera could not agree, so they decided to consult Tiresias. Having made love as both a man and a woman, he was in an excellent position to judge. Tiresias stated that, according to his experience, women can reach a climax nine times more often than men. Hera was furious at his indiscretion – Tiresias had revealed the secret of women's orgasmic superiority! To punish him, she struck him blind. As compensation, Zeus promised him a long life, and gave him the gift of prophecy.

For centuries, most civilisations have seen women brutally and unjustly dominated by men. The unconscious motivation for this seems to be a profound male envy of the orgasmic superiority of women.

Men are ridden with anxiety at the idea of not being able to fully satisfy their women. That is why in some parts of Africa, ritual excision of the clitoris is still practised. The clitoris has no other biological function except to heighten women's pleasure during orgasm. So in some traditions it is considered judicious to amputate the clitoris of young girls, so that they will not have any pleasure during sex. This, in turn, will remove any temptation to be unfaithful when they are married. They must content themselves with bringing a number of children into the world, preferably male children.

Nothing could be farther from the Taoist attitude than this kind of violent intervention, designed to inhibit the orgasmic potential of women. According to the Taoist principle of Yin and Yang, the feminine and the masculine energies represent opposite but equal poles. If the woman is constantly dissatisfied, the couple cannot attain the harmony of true love.

Taoists believe that a sexually-frustrated woman brings bad luck to a household or business. Frigidity leads to psychological sterility, which affects the man just as much as the woman. On the other hand, a satisfied woman possesses a kind of positive magnetism which attracts happiness and prosperity. That is why the Taoists developed techniques which enable men to strengthen their sexual prowess.

WHAT ARE THE SIGNS OF FEMALE PLEASURE AND ORGASM?

In the same way that men can be compared to fire, women can be compared to water: they need time before coming to a boil. It is therefore important for men to be able to see and feel their partner's orgasm coming on, in order to avoid premature ejaculation, which will leave the woman dissatisfied. Some of you may be familiar with the Masters and Johnson description of orgasm. But you may find it interesting to see how the ancient Chinese described – in a way that was perfectly accurate as well as poetic – the progressive ascent of pleasure in women.

In a work entitled *Admirable Conversations Between the Yellow Emperor and the Daughter of Candour,* the Emperor asks his Taoist governess how he can recognise the female orgasm. The Daughter of Candour explains:

"The man must watch for various signs in the woman, and act accordingly. First, the woman's face blushes, and her ears become hot. This shows that her mind is excited by the idea of amorous contact. Her perfumed body is extended on a couch; her limbs are tense and immobile. Her nostrils are dilated. This indicates her desire to receive the Jade Peak. The man can now begin the act gently, as if playing a game. He penetrates her just a bit, and waits to observe her reactions.

"Her eyes and eyebrows start moving. The tips of her breasts grow hard. This means she is excited. The Jade Peak can now be pushed to the midway point of the Deep Valley.

"When her voice becomes hoarse, as if her throat were dry, her desire is fully aroused. Her eyes are closed, and she breathes heavily. At this time, the Jade Peak can begin to move freely. Their communion is well on the path to ecstasy.

"Her tongue sticks out as if she were half asleep or drunk. This shows that her Red Pearl (vulva) craves the alternating deep and shallow thrusts of the Jade Peak.

"Her Red Pearl becomes very moist and slippery as her desire is about to reach its zenith; each thrust of the man stirs her fluids. Her body arches up and clings to his. Her feet and toes are tense, and she tries to hold the Jade Peak inside her. She murmurs in a husky voice. She can no longer control the trembling in her voice. This indicates the rising of the Yin tide.

"She begins perspiring lightly, smiling all the while. This means she doesn't want the man to stop, as her pleasure is still growing. When the Yin tide flows in, she begins shaking. Her Red Pearl secretes an abundance of fluid. Her whole body burns and becomes wet with perspiration.

"Finally, her hands and feet relax. Her eyes are closed as if in deep sleep, or as if she were under a spell. Her body is limp, her limbs completely relaxed. This means that she is now fulfilled."

THE ART OF TOUCHING

a. Ethereal massage

Without any further ado, let's get down to the pre-liminaries. Concentrate on what you're doing. If you love the woman you're with, show her that you do by giving her all your attention. Once undressed, you can begin the lovemaking session with an ethereal massage. The ethereal (astral) body represents the energy flowing in and around a person's physical body. Its existence has been conclusively demonstrated by the photographer Kirlian. It envelopes the physical body and radiates, more or less brightly, depending on the individual's energy level. Here's how to perform an ethereal massage:

After taking a few slow, deep breaths, rub your hands vigorously together. Concentrate all your energy in your hands, which will begin to radiate heat and magnetism. Now run both your hands very lightly over the various parts of your partner's body. You should hardly touch her skin at all. Transmit your feelings of love through the magnetism in your hands. This kind of subtle massage will stimulate your partner's ethereal body, and fill her with a delicious sensation of well-being. The very gentle touching will make her feel confident and relaxed, and she will find it much easier to let herself go.

When it's your turn to receive an ethereal massage, be receptive to the love your partner is transmitting through her hands. Feel your ethereal body being charged with magnetic energy.

b. Physical massage and reflexology

Women take longer to become sexually aroused than men. The erogenous zones in her genitals are less localised, and the excitement she feels is more diffuse, involving her entire body, and depending on both her present state of mind and the feelings she has for her partner. Penetration without any preliminaries may not be sufficient to induce orgasm. This can even be painful if the vagina is not lubricated enough, which takes time.

A vigorous massage is an excellent prelude to actual penetration. It improves blood circulation and reduces stress. Be firm but gentle. Spend a lot of time on the neck and shoulders, where a lot of tension tends to accumulate during the course of a day.

If you massage the meridians on one side of the body, it's always a good idea to do the other side as well. The body's symmetry must be respected. If you massage the left foot, don't forget to do the right one as well.

Intuition is important when giving a massage. But, at least in the beginning, ask your partner to express what she finds pleasing, and what pleases her less. Would she like you to press more lightly on a certain point, or more firmly on another? This will help you become familiar with the particularities of her erogenous zones, and bring you into harmony with her body.

Reciprocity is important in love. You have to know how to give, and also how to take. Let your partner massage you as well. Abandon yourself to the care of her hands. Guide her with a few remarks on what you like, and what you don't like. If she isn't confident in her ability to massage, be very complimentary. Massage is more a question of intuition and good intentions than it is of technique.

Both physical and magnetic massages help men learn to control their impatience, which is the main cause of premature ejaculation. In fact, massage helps establish contact on a physical and energetic level that goes far beyond pure genital stimulation. It also liberates you from being egoistic and selfish, which is another potential cause of premature ejaculation.

Massage is often a better way to begin making love than engaging in the usual, drawn-out preliminaries which are supposed to arouse women (and men as well!). Even caresses which are usually stimulating under normal conditions will have little or no effect if your partner is tense or preoccupied. Massage will harmonise your partner's energy, and open her body so that it becomes more receptive to erotic caresses.

Massage is also very useful during recuperation periods between coitus. It will renew both your desire, and your partner's.

c. Caressing, like any art, requires creativity

When it comes to caressing, you should make use of all your creativity. An infinite variety of contact is possible, using the mouth and nose. With your faces in close embrace, you can rub noses like the Eskimos, or press lips and tongues together in a full French kiss. You can stroke, lick, bite, squeeze and press every part of your partner's body, or even use your warm breath to caress her. Vary your caresses, and the order in which you use them – you don't want your amorous encounters to become routine. In short, never caress your partner mechanically, as if it were a task you have to perform before penetration.

Sucking your partner's nipples is pleasing to both of you. And Taoists see this as a way of absorbing large quantities of Yin energy, which has an extremely invigorating effect.

Remember that women are less centred on genital stimulation than men. A woman's entire body can be considered an erogenous zone. Stimulating the breasts does increase vaginal stimulation, and can help women attain an orgasm. But there are other areas of the female body which are often ignored, like the earlobes, or the nape of the neck.

If you happen to have long hair, use it to caress your partner's inner and outer thighs. You can also do this with your penis.

d. Cunnilingus and fellatio

Many women enjoy these very intimate forms of caress, and the art of Chinese eroticism makes full use of the practice of oral stimulation. The ancient Chinese produced poetic and very graphic descriptions of these acts which, for many people here in the West, are still subjects of shame and repulsion. The Chinese call cunnilingus (stimulating the female genitals with the tongue) carrying fire to the mountain. Fellatio (using the mouth to caress the penis) is referred to as the art of playing the flute.

Most of us have long since rid ourselves of the taboos associated with these acts. The Chinese had no reservations about representing them in their various art forms. One print, for example, shows the Empress Wu Hu (Tang dynasty) holding her robe open while a high dignitary performs cunnilingus on her hypertrophied sex. This monarch seems to have been irritated by the importance accorded to fellatio, and ordered her courtiers to show their homage by performing cunnilingus on her.

However, Taoist texts recommend that men do not allow women to perform fellatio on them in the early stages of sexual relations. The caress is so stimulating that it can easily lead to premature ejaculation. On the other hand, the same texts claim that cunnilingus can cure impotence when practised on highly-excitable women, who produce abundant vaginal secretions. Oriental erotic art considers the act a ritual way of honouring the gateway of existence. Cunnilingus, therefore, acquired a semi-sacred quality. It is also another excellent way for men to absorb the Yin energy emitted by their female partners.

If your partner is willing to perform fellatio, then it would be hard not to reciprocate with cunnilingus, without appearing impolite or selfish. And remember that the tongue is much better than the fingers for caressing the female sex, since there is no risk of irritating the mucous membranes around the clitoris, which are extremely sensitive. Women love this form of caress, which often leads to a full orgasm.

THE G-POINT

Don't forget to stimulate the famous G-point, which more and more people are discovering, and which was already well-known to the ancients. This erotic reflex point was discovered by the German gynaecologist Ernst Grafenberg (from whence it gets its name: G-point). It is situated on the anterior vaginal wall, slightly past the midway point. It is not always perceptible when women are not aroused, and sometimes strong pressure is needed to stimulate it. In the West, this erogenous zone has, to a large extent, been anaesthetised by cultural ignorance. Don't be surprised if your partner doesn't feel anything at first.

A number of attempts are often required to arouse the zone. Your partner may even want to resort to masturbation, in order to learn how to arouse her G-point herself. But if you persevere, the results will be well worth the effort. Stimulating this point produces much more intense orgasms than those obtained through clitoral or vaginal stimulation.

You can stimulate the G-point manually, during foreplay. During coitus, penetration from the rear makes it easier to stimulate the point with the penis. Another good position is having your partner sit on you while you are stretched out on your back. Here, the woman does the moving, and she can direct your penis so that her G-point is stimulated to the maximum.

In their book entitled *The G-Point*, Ladas, Whipple and Perry report that this type of orgasm often results in an intense tightening of the vagina, which literally squeezes the penis (or finger) of the male partner out.

The Second Secret

◆

Making love in the present moment

As you may have noticed, lovemaking is often done in haste. It's almost as if people were trying to use the act to get rid of excess tension, instead of making love for the sake of making love. Such encounters are not very nourishing, and can leave you feeling empty, and even somewhat bitter. Hasty lovemaking also has unpleasant consequences, notably premature ejaculation in men and frigidity in women. This occurs because we are often not fully aware of the present moment when making love.

HERE AND NOW

Lao Tsu, in his *Tao Te King*, humorously said, "My teaching is seen as madness in the eyes of ordinary men." This is because he refused to be like everyone else. People spend their lives preparing for some future happiness, which they always seem to put off for tomorrow. Lao Tsu tells us to live in the here and now. Those who want to be happy, can only do so here and now. The present moment is the only reality. It is eternal. And there is nothing else.

Most religions speak about paradise as if it were another world, accessible only after death. In Taoism, paradise too is here and now, precisely where we are at the present moment.

For modern man, coitus is a special opportunity to experience the present moment. According to Taoism, the sexual experience cannot be reduced to an expedient exercise in physical and mental hygiene, or to a course in achieving orgasm, in order to reinforce some egoistic desire for power or approval.

Make love without any aim whatsoever, whether it be to have an orgasm or affirm your virility. In this way, caressing does not become some kind of preliminary obligation, or a polite way of helping a partner who is slow in reaching her climax, attain satisfaction. Any gesture, even a gentle touch or look, is enough to induce the state of ecstasy . . . and without ejaculation!

It's like making love with the present moment itself. The whole environment participates in the experience, the colours of the room, the music you play, the odours you inhale . . . all give you pleasure. The singing of the birds outside, the plants in your room. You no longer feel separated from the great current of Tao that pervades everything that is.

HOW AN AWARENESS OF THE PRESENT MOMENT CAN RESOLVE YOUR SEXUAL PROBLEMS

When you are able to relax totally in the present moment, problems of impotence or premature ejaculation will disappear.

Impotence

Let's look at impotence, or the inability to maintain an erection. If all you want is to get an erection at any cost, you are creating tension in your mind. Relax, and try to forget about your own pleasure. Start breathing deeply and slowly. Then start caressing and stimulating your partner. Be very aware of what you are doing. Concentrate on the currents of energy or heat circulating in your hands. Then feel your hands touching your partner's body. Feel the burning heat in her body. Breathe in the odour of her perfume. Listen to her sighs of pleasure as you caress her.

If you can really forget yourself, your partner's arousal will be transferred to you through a process of osmosis. You will become erect without making any effort at all, simply by making love in the present moment.

Premature ejaculation

Premature ejaculation can also be prevented by being acutely conscious of the present moment. The problem is often caused by a kind of nervous excitement that is present in everything you do. In fact, you are moving too fast.

As suggested earlier, start a lovemaking session by performing a physical or magnetic massage. This will help you experience the sensations in your own body on a more subtle level. You will degenitalise your desire, which will be diffused through your entire body, instead of remaining localised in the few square centimetres of skin covering your penis. In a way, your whole body becomes a penis, which vibrates intensely in all its parts.

You will soon notice your mind concentrating around the area of your stomach. Your pleasure will acquire a new centre of gravity, which is much more stable – it will be anchored in the deepest part of your being. And in this state, penetration will no longer represent the drop which causes your cup to overflow.

The Third Secret

◆

Harmonising Yin and Yang in yourself

This section is about inner attitude or awareness. What you must understand is that as long as you are not in harmony with the female principle in yourself, you will not be able to find harmony with any female outside yourself. Femininity is a little like the hidden part of your character. As long as you refuse to explore this hidden side, you will fear women. You will not really be able to understand their needs, and thus you will be incapable of fully satisfying them. Many sexual problems arise because of an erroneous conception of what virility and femininity are.

WHAT IS REAL VIRILITY?

Lao Tsu warns men to guard against a false conception of virility. From a Taoist point of view, real virility consists of not fearing the female principle in yourself. Men should not force themselves to constantly be aggressive and dominating. There are times when they should give free rein to their innate capacity for gentleness and receptivity.

Masculine qualities can be compared to the right leg of the body, while female qualities can be represented by the left leg. No one wants to be a one-legged cripple! Female qualities, when harmoniously combined with male qualities, allow you to move forward without limping along on one leg only.

Real force or power is never brutal.

It is the result of a perfect combination of firmness and suppleness, of will-power and relaxation. Judo is a good example. Instead of directly resisting the attacks of a powerful opponent, the opponent's own brutal strength is channelled back and used against him, and only in this way can he be beaten. The slender branches of a tree, weighed down with snow, do not break. In fact, they offer no resistance, and keep bending under the weight until the snow finally falls off.

The same principle applies to sexuality. Controlling ejaculation or erection cannot be achieved through forced effort, but by the result of a serene mind.

THE INTERPLAY OF YIN AND YANG

The infinite energy of Tao is present everywhere and in all things, in the form of two opposite and equal poles – Yin and Yang – negative and positive, feminine and masculine, water and fire, earth and sky, life and death, good and bad . . . The poles are not really in opposition to each other – they are, in fact, complementary. One cannot exist without the other.

It is the interplay of Yin and Yang which animates life on all levels. Without this permanent tension between two opposite and equal poles, nothing would exist. The poles are found in human beings, just as they exist on a cosmic level of planets and galaxies. Each of us is a microcosm of the entire universe.

Taoism uses the figure of a circle as a symbol for Yin and Yang. Black Yin and white Yang are in constant movement inside the circle. What is of special significance is the presence of a small white circle in the middle of the black Yin side, and a small black circle in the middle of the white Yang side. This, of course, shows that in each man there is place for the feminine principle, and vice versa. Women are predominantly Yin, men predominantly Yang. However, no one is exclusively Yin or Yang.

EQUALITY OF THE SEXES

Theories which claim that women are inferior to men are absurd. If we talk about electricity, can we say that the negative pole is less important than the positive? The same goes for masculine and feminine. They are absolutely equal. And this applies to sexuality between couples as well. For Taoists, the female orgasm is just as important as the male orgasm.

When Yin and Yang unite, there is balance and harmony. When men and women make love with an attitude of mutual respect, the exchange of their energies is beneficial to both. Coming into contact with the opposite pole is a challenge which stimulates the entire organism. By uniting their feminine and masculine qualities, men and women gain health and longevity. To achieve this, however, sexual contact must be profound and prolonged.

HOW TO HARMONISE
YIN AND YANG
DURING COITUS

Taoists have studied and perfected the communion between Yin and Yang, unimpeded by any inhibitions of false modesty. Here are some of their observations on the subject:

- When you cease being afraid of women, it is much easier to retain your sperm, and maintain an erection. As we have said, anxiety caused by an obsession about performance, is one of the major causes of premature ejaculation and impotence.

- To free yourself of your fears while making love with a woman, you should remember that this woman is both outside and inside you at the same time. Try to experience her as if she were a part of yourself. Be one with her, experiencing both a physical and psychological union. Try to feel as if you were alone with yourself. Imagine that you are your own partner.

- By identifying too much with your active male principle, you risk getting too excited and setting off the ejaculatory mechanism. This is an ancient reflex, deeply engraved in your genetic code. To control it, try to be more passive and receptive, as if you were a woman. Feel the pleasure penetrating your body. Don't fabricate pleasure by seeking images and fantasies in your mind. Let it enter you, as if through osmosis, as you feel the joy your partner is experiencing through contact with you.

- By identifying yourself with the female orgasm, you can forget about your own, and thus retain your sperm much more easily. Feel the discharge of her energy entering your body. In this way, you can even have an orgasm without ejaculating, and this a number of times in succession. This is the great secret of implosive (or valley) orgasm as promised by Taoist teaching.

- Uniting with the female principle in no way diminishes your virility. In fact, the aim is not to emphasise one pole over another, but to harmonise Yin and Yang within yourself. In other words, to become aware of the universal interplay of Yin and Yang as it occurs inside your mind and body.

- Ultimately, sexual control depends to a large extent on being able to maintain the subtle balance between Yin and Yang. In practice, this means being able to be both passive and active, receiver and sender, soft and firm, static and dynamic. It requires a great degree of suppleness, which is one of the most important feminine qualities.

The Fourth Secret

◆

Union of the Jade Peak and the Deep Valley

We now come to the crucial point – penetration. It's better to wait for the woman to invite penetration, verbally or through some physical sign. She can even grasp your penis in her hand and guide it into her vagina herself, which will avoid any clumsy efforts. This will also help you maintain your erection if it is weak, or if you are nervous.

MAKING THE
THREE LIQUIDS FLOW

Before penetration, make sure that the vagina is well-lubricated. Try not to use saliva or any other substance to make penetration easier. The reason why is explained in this beautiful passage from a Chinese erotic novel:

"[. . .] he raised his Jade Peak and used it to caress the opening of Yi-Hiang's garden. Not only did he dare not enter, he didn't even stay near the opening; instead, he explored the avenue between her legs. What do you think this meant? It is the procedure for breaking the rock and getting the spring water to flow. Nothing is more slippery than a woman's secretions. It is Nature's gift for lubricating a man's Jade Peak, and the female sex. Although saliva is also effective, it cannot compare with (vaginal) secretions. Men who use their saliva are impatient. Nothing can replace the liquid which flows from the source itself, both in quality and effectiveness." (*The Flesh Is A Sacred Carpet,* by Li-Yu.)

It is interesting to note that the ancient Taoists claimed three waters (lunar flower water) flow from the Deep Valley (vagina). The first water is the lubricating liquid which facilitates penetration. The second corresponds to secretions which occur during ordinary orgasm. The third is related to a much more curious phenomenon, which has also been observed by modern sexologists. It refers to the very abundant secretion which occurs during the intense orgasm produced by stimulating the G-point.

The liquid is secreted with such force that sexologists have called it female ejaculation. It is so abundant that women who are unaware of the phenomenon may believe they are actually urinating! However, this third water is not urine, but a liquid that closely resembles the secretions produced by a man's prostate gland.

BE ONE WITH
YOUR PENIS

Penetration is an art. Invest in your penis. Feel the intense energy it emits, and the pleasure it gives your partner. Concentrate on the present moment. Feel yourself penetrating your partner mentally as well as physically. You must not give her the impression that your head is elsewhere, that you're thinking about someone or something else ... least of all another woman! The intimate contact of your genitals creates an intense energy field. Feel the energy circulating between and around you both.

LEARNING TO EXPLORE THE SUBTLETIES OF PENETRATION

Since Western men have been more accustomed to quick sex than long, drawn-out lovemaking, they have had little time to explore the subtleties of penetration. They have limited themselves to a more or less mechanical thrusting, with little nuance or variation. However, it is possible to be very creative as far as penetration is concerned.

Li Tong-hsuan, a Chinese doctor who lived in the seventh century A.D. provides us with an excellent insight into the expertise that can be acquired in this area:

"Deep and shallow, slow and rapid, straight and oblique, all these thrusts are in no way the same, and each possesses its own characteristics and effects. Slow thrusting resembles the movement of a carp as it plays with a fisherman's hook; rapid thrusting is like the flight of a bird against the wind. Entering and withdrawing, stirring from top to bottom, from left to right, pausing at times, and then thrusting in rapid succession ... all these movements should relate to each other. Each should be used at the right moment, and no one style should be used exclusively, just because it gives you more momentary pleasure."

DIFFERENT TYPES OF PENETRATION AND MOVEMENT IN THE VAGINA

In ancient erotic manuals written for newly-weds, we find more precise directions. They deal not only with the various types of movement in the vagina, but also with different ways of introducing the penis into the vagina. Here's how they are described, during a very beautiful conversation between the Yellow Emperor and his governess, the Daughter of Candour:

When the Yellow Emperor asked the Daughter of Candour to explain the different ways of penetrating the vagina, she enumerated six techniques:

I   "Push the Jade Peak downwards and let it come and go over the strings of the lute like a saw, as if it were being used to force open an oyster in order to extract its brilliant pearl."

II "Push against the golden ravine above the veins of jade, as if you were splitting apart a rock to discover its jade core."

III "Strike the Terrace of Pleasure (clitoris) hard with the Jade Peak, like a steel pestle thrusting down into a mortar."

IV   "Enter and withdraw the Jade Peak and strike the Examination Room (the sides of the vulva) on the right and left, as if beating hot iron with a hammer."

V   "Turn the Jade Peak around in the Sacred Field and Deep Valley, like a farmer digging up his fields in autumn."

VI   "Let the Jade Peak and Red Pearl (vulva) meet tumultuously, like two avalanches crashing into each other."

When the Yellow Emperor enquired as to the various ways of moving the penis in the vagina, the Daughter of Candour described the nine forms of movement in the vagina:

I   "Strike to the left and to the right, like a courageous warrior fighting through the ranks of his enemies."

II   "Move the Jade Peak up and down, like a wild horse jumping over a raging river."

III   "Withdraw and thrust like a flock of seagulls playing in the waves."

IV   "Rapidly alternate shallow and deep thrusts, like a raven pecking at grains of rice in a bowl."

V   "Perform a regular series of deep and shallow thrusts, like small and large stones sinking in the ocean."

VI   "Enter like a serpent gliding into its den for its winter sleep."

VII "Make little, rapid thrusts, like a frightened rat running into its burrow."

VIII "Withdraw slowly as if there were a weight tied to your feet, or like an eagle burdened in flight with its prey. Then plunge like an eagle swooping down to grab its prey in its talons."

IX   "Withdraw, then thrust forward like a graceful sailing ship, plunging through the waves into the wind."

Of course, some of the comparisons stretch the limits of poetic licence, but they do demonstrate the refined attitude the Chinese had towards the sexual act. In any case, you can certainly find some inspiration in these verses, both for yourself and your partner.

NINE SHALLOW THRUSTS, ONE DEEP THRUST

The technique most highly recommended by Taoists is to alternate nine shallow thrusts with one deep thrust, since they believe this is the rhythm most likely to satisfy women.

Also, adopting a regular rhythm during penetration is an excellent way to circulate sexual energy through your entire body. The number 9 is the most sacred Yang number. Nine thrusts allow you to accumulate Yang energy in your *hara* (energy centre situated in the solar plexus). If you only use deep thrusts, you risk losing control and ejaculating too quickly.

Women enjoy shallow thrusts, since they stimulate the middle part of the vagina, and make the deep thrust that follows all that more intense. Shallow thrusting builds up excitement in women, and considerably increases their level of arousal.

SIZE OF THE
JADE PEAK

Many men worry about the size and shape of their penis when erect. Is it too short or too thin to fully satisfy their partner? This anxiety was known to the ancient Chinese. The Yellow Emperor asked the Daughter of Candour about it: "Does the size and shape of the Jade Peak affect the pleasure of sexual union?"

Here's what she had to say:

"Differences in size and form are what are visible on the outside. The real beauty and pleasure of union are manifest inside. If men associate sexual union primarily with love and respect for women, and if they take what they are doing to heart, then how could a minor difference in size or form change anything?

"A long, large member that is always semi-soft is worth less than a short, thin member that is hard. A firm, hard member that is brutally introduced is worth less than a weak, soft member that is used delicately and gently."

As we can see, there are no predetermined criteria regarding the size of the penis. A man whose erect penis is short should not develop a complex about it. And in fact, if his partner's vagina is rather small, she is much better off than with someone who has a very long penis. The sexual organs of both sexes must be proportional. If a man's penis is too long he may, when overly excited, push too far and press on the neck of the uterus, or even penetrate the uterus itself, which is hardly pleasant for the woman, especially if she finds her uterus inflamed because of it.

Obviously, if a woman's vagina is long, a long penis will suit her very well. If her vagina is wide, than a thick penis will be best. It all depends on both partners' anatomy. And in the final analysis, the feelings two people have for one another are more important than the size of their genitals.

IS IT POSSIBLE TO MAKE THE PENIS LONGER OR THICKER?

If the preceding statements have not reassured you, don't be discouraged: it is possible to enlarge the penis to some extent.

Like any muscle, the penis requires exercise. A penis that is not used often, that is always imprisoned in a pair of tight jeans or underwear, will not have much chance to develop. And if the only occasions you allow it to hang free are the brief excursions you take into your partner's vagina, then it will never assume its full dimension.

The techniques described in this book will help you have prolonged and vigorous erections. This results in more blood being pumped into the tip of the penis, and remaining there for long periods of time. This fact alone helps expand the erectile tissue, which is criss-crossed with innumerable tiny blood-vessels.

The technique of squeezing the base of the penis or the testicles after ejaculation also has the same effect, especially if you apply strong pressure to the point midway between the anus and the testicles. This blocks the draining of blood out of the penis, and maintains a high degree of dilation of the erectile tissue. It will also help you regain your erection in a shorter period of time.

Taoists also recommend the following techniques when you masturbate:

- Squeeze the penis while moving your hand from the base to the top, as if you were milking it. This sends more blood into the tip.

- When the penis is erect, squeeze hard on the base to make it harder. At the same time, press on the point situated midway between the anus and the testicles. By dilating your penis to the maximum, it will gradually take the shape of a mushroom, which seems to be more enjoyable to women than a penis that is straight, like a finger or pencil.

- Whether your penis is soft or erect, rub it between the palms of your hands. "He rubs his Jade Peak in his hands, in the same way that you would separate a single rope into many strands", said Wou-hien, an ancient Chinese doctor.

- Spread your thighs apart. Take your penis on your hand and use it to slap one of your thighs 25 to 50 times. Be firm but not rough. Do the same on the other thigh. Then continue, alternating from one thigh to the other.

- A variation of this consists of getting down on all fours, with your legs slightly apart. Then, by moving your lower back, start your penis swinging back and forth so that it strikes your abdomen.

Even if you're not trying to lengthen or enlarge your penis, these exercises will benefit you by:

- improving blood circulation in your penis;

- stimulating reflexology points on your penis;

- giving you harder and more rapid erections (which is helpful for those who have certain problems with their erections);

- desensitising your member to some extent (useful for those who tend to ejaculate too quickly);

- allowing you to regain your erection more rapidly (useful for older men who need more time to become erect after ejaculating).

THE INCONVENIENCES
OF CONDOMS

A condom greatly reduces the risks of conception and genital infection. Unfortunately, the synthetic materials used to make condoms completely block any exchange of fluids between partners. This has a very negative effect on the interaction between Yin and Yang.

Women hardly feel the intense energy emitted by the penis. And many men claim that wearing a condom considerably diminishes their genital pleasure. Thus, the flow of biomagnetic energy between partners is disturbed.

WHAT TO DO
IN THE CASE OF
IMPOTENCE OR
WEAK ERECTIONS

It may happen that you are not able to get an erection, or that the erection you do get is too weak to permit penetration. If you let yourself get anxious about it, this kind of temporary failure can develop into complete psychological impotence.

The first thing to do is to start breathing deeply and slowly. This will calm your sympathetic nervous system which, when hyperactive, causes anxiety and, in turn, stimulate your parasympathetic system, which is responsible for erections. You can also practice a technique called the inner smile, while your partner stimulates you.

Long before Masters and Johnson, Taoists recommended the following strategy: forget about your penis. Don't think about your problem with getting an erection. Dedicate yourself completely to giving pleasure to your partner. Caress her, massage her, stimulate her erogenous zones. Her arousal will gradually be transmitted to you through osmosis. As you lose yourself in the erotic excitement of the moment, you will suddenly find that your penis is fully erect. Getting an erection is an unconscious process, and you will only make things worse by trying to use will-power to force yourself to become erect.

If your erection is weak, you can increase its hardness by squeezing your penis firmly around the base. You will then have no trouble penetrating your partner.

Another technique: use your fingers to support your penis while inserting it into your partner's vagina. In both cases, once you are inside the vagina, your thrusting movements will be so stimulating that your penis will very quickly become fully erect.

MASTERING
SEXUAL POSITIONS

The different sexual positions are the spice of love. The variety of possible positions is so vast that couples need never get the feeling their lovemaking is routine, even after being together for years. Change positions, or move smoothly from one to another. Find out which ones excite you most, and which provide the most pleasure to both of you simultaneously. Also remember the positions in which you can best control your ejaculation.

It is certainly possible to stick to one position. But the Taoist approach leads to lovemaking sessions which are of particularly long duration. Muscular fatigue or cramps may result if you don't change positions.

We will now take a look at the five basic positions, and their respective advantages.

1. Man on top of the woman.

2. Woman on top of the man.

3. Man penetrates the woman from the rear.

4. Man and woman face each other in a lateral position.

5. Man sitting, with the woman sitting on him.

Most other positions are variations of these five basic positions.

1. Direct union (Missionary)

The best-known position in the West is called the missionary position: the woman lies on her back, with the man on top of her.

Both bodies are in contact, from the tips of the toes right up to the face. This creates a large area of tactile stimulation, and also allows mouth and eye contact. The position is pleasant for women, as long as the man is not too heavy. Every movement the man makes is a caress, as his body rubs on the woman's breasts and thighs. Women can use their hands to caress the man's shoulders, back and buttocks. If she feels the penetration is not deep enough with her legs straight, she can raise them comfortably to an angle of about 45 degrees. This is called the silk roll position.

2. Unalterable attachment (Amazon)

Here the man lies on his back and the woman mounts him. The advantage for women is that they can control their movements and get the precise kind of genital stimulation that will bring them to orgasm. Even frigid women can experience orgasm if their partner allows them to adopt this position.

The man remains passive. He can enjoy the spectacle of his partner taking her pleasure, or close his eyes and just let himself go.

Many men find this position helpful for controlling ejaculation. Masters and Johnson recommend it for this reason, and have even integrated it into their therapy for premature ejaculation. In contrast, the missionary position can speed up ejaculation.

In the reverse Amazon position, the woman turns her back to the man before sitting on his penis. She retains the same freedom of movement as in the frontal Amazon position. Here the man can caress her buttocks and back with his hands. In ancient texts, this position is called the reverse flying ducks position.

3. The unicorn's horn (Doggy)

In this position, the woman is on all fours, with the man on his knees behind her, penetrating her from the rear.

Its animal connotation makes the position very exciting. Men should be careful not to let themselves ejaculate too quickly, as monkeys do. Some women don't like the position because they feel it isn't very romantic. Others find it the best way to have an orgasm. And, in fact, it does make stimulation of the famous G-point, situated on the anterior wall of the vagina, easier.

4. The gills of the exposed fish (Lateral)

Both the man and woman lie on their side, face to face. The advantage of the lateral position is that neither one has to bear the weight of the other. With the help of cushions, they can stay in this position for a very long time. It is calm and meditative, and conducive to performing energy circulation exercises.

5. The cry of the monkey embracing a tree (Sitting)

The man sits with his legs crossed or straight out in front of him. The woman sits on him, wrapping her legs around his waist. Both partners wrap their arms around the other's back. Supported in this way, the position is remarkably comfortable. The spine remains straight, making it easier for energy to rise up from the genitals and spread through the rest of the body. Couples are also face to face, and can even press their foreheads together. This is ideal for fusing Yin and

Yang energies, so that the circle of energy around the couple becomes almost tangible. The sitting position does not allow for much movement of the genitals, but it does make for a more spiritually profound sexual experience. It is also excellent for men who have trouble retaining their ejaculation.

The Fifth Secret

◆

The virtues
of breathing

CORRECT BREATHING

Of all the organisms' functions, breathing is the most vital. We can do without food or water for days, but how long can a person live without air? A few minutes at most. Therefore, we cannot overemphasise the importance of deep breathing.

Aside from staying alive, breathing is of fundamental importance on two other levels:

- Taoists discovered that deep breathing is the basis of good general health. Breathing from the abdomen rather than the chest helps create vital energy or *chi*. It is also in the abdomen that *chi* energy accumulates. So abdominal breathing is a simple and inexpensive way to maintain your general health and sexual vigour.

- Breathing also plays a central role in sexual control. Deep, harmonious breathing helps balance and relax the sympathetic nervous system. If this system is tense, you will lose your erection, or ejaculate prematurely.

As you may have noticed, anxiety makes your heartbeat and your breathing accelerate. Blood pressure rises. Breathing becomes shallow, filling only the upper part of the lungs. If you slow your breathing down and breathe more deeply, your heartbeat will also slow down, and your blood vessels will dilate. This intake of fresh oxygen eliminates anxiety and its harmful effects on sexual functions.

HOW TO BREATHE CORRECTLY ACCORDING TO TAOIST TEACHING

To practice deep breathing, sit comfortably in a quiet place. Straighten your spine and keep your back very straight. Relax the muscles in your shoulders by massaging them or moving them in a circular motion. You can also relax your neck by slowly rotating your head a few times. Now you are ready to begin. Close your eyes. First, exhale as much as you can, in order to become more aware of your breathing, and to empty your lungs completely.

Now breathe in through your nose (not your mouth, unless it is impossible for you to do so, in which case use your mouth). As you inhale, feel your abdomen expanding – yes, your abdomen and not your lungs is the first to be filled with air. When the abdomen is fully expanded, continue inhaling until your lungs are full as well. This comprises one complete inhalation. Hold the breath for a couple of seconds, then exhale slowly, and completely. Repeat the process for a few minutes.

EFFECTS OF 'EMBRYONIC' BREATHING

Taoists call this type of breathing 'embryonic', since the aim of the method is to make you feel reborn after each meditation session. In a text called the *Tai-si Keou Kiue* (Oral Instruction On Embryonic Breathing) we find the following:

"By practising embryonic breathing, we return to the basis of life, to our origins, chasing away old age and returning to the state of the foetus."

This exercise of slow, deep breathing will relax and revitalise you. It will improve your resistance to stress. Try to practice it for a few minutes each day. Remember, breathing is life. *Chi* energy will accumulate around your navel, which the Orientals consider to be the vital centre of the entire organism. Thus, the foetus receives all its energy directly through the umbilical cord.

Be aware of the movements of your diaphragm as you practise the deep breathing exercise. Abdominal breathing massages the internal organs, as the abdominal muscles are brought into play.

SOME OTHER WAYS TO USE BREATHING DURING COITUS

You can intensify or control sexual energy during coitus through conscious breathing. Here are some of the techniques recommended by the old Taoist texts:

- Try reversing your breathing during coitus. When you thrust with your penis, the natural tendency is to breathe out. You can modify this conditioned reflex by consciously breathing in instead. The effect is twofold – it helps prevent ejaculation, and also allows you to extract the vitality of your own sperm and nourish your body.

- Breathe as much as possible from the abdomen. Exhale as slowly as possible, imagining that you are getting rid of the excess desire inside you. If necessary, suspend your breathing completely for a moment. This will stop the flow of your thoughts and, in turn, the movement of sperm, which depends, to a large extent, on your degree of mental agitation.

- Press your tongue to your palate and inhale deeply and vigorously, with your mouth open. Feel the current of cold air entering your mouth and creating a sensation of cold on the mucous membranes (especially those under the tongue). Concentrate on this sensation of cold to calm your mind, and feel it spreading through your body.

The Sixth Secret

◆

The 'stag' exercise

The Taoists were great observers of nature, and noticed that stags (male deer) demonstrated a high degree of sexual prowess and fecundity. They also noticed that when a stag exposes his sex, he simultaneously contracts his anus. From this they developed the stag exercise.

In this exercise, you work with your pubiococcygeal muscles, which run from the coccyx to the pubis, and include the muscles responsible for anal and perineal contraction, as well as those which surround the penis.

A network of nerves, called the *plexus honteux,* runs through the pubiococcygeal muscle group, which transmits all stimulation in the genital area to the brain. It also acts as a receiver for pleasure signals emitted by the brain. These signals result in rhythmic contractions which set off the mechanism of ejaculation.

As modern sexology has shown, the PC muscle group plays an important role in controlling ejaculation and orgasm. American sexologists have nicknamed it the 'love muscle'. It has been proven that a weakness of this muscle can seriously affect a person's sex life. In men, this usually takes the form of premature ejaculation and/or prostate problems. Frigid women have been able to experience orgasm after strengthening their weak pubiococcygeal muscles.

Once again, science has confirmed what was known intuitively by the ancient Taoists. But this knowledge has even greater repercussions than our Western sexologists imagine.

STAG EXERCISE: FIRST VARIATION

Sit on a chair, or on the floor with your legs crossed. Straighten your spine and keep your back very straight.

Contract all the muscles in your genital-anal area at the same time as you inhale. To reinforce the contraction, imagine that your are inhaling through your anus. After a few seconds of maximum tension, release all the muscles and exhale slowly. Repeat this cycle of intense muscle contraction and breathing 20 times.

Once you are familiar with the stag exercise, you can practice it anywhere. Use dead periods of time, for example, when waiting in line, or stuck in a traffic jam. You can do the exercise seated or standing up, and no one will know the difference. Instead of getting impatient when you have to wait, take advantage of the opportunity to strengthen your love muscle!

SECOND VARIATION

This is a more advanced version of the stag exercise. Here you learn to differentiate the various muscles which make up the pubiococcygeal group, and which play an essential role in controlling ejaculation. You will contract the urogenital muscles separately from those around the anus. Here's what to do:

• Rub your palms vigorously together. When they are hot, use your right hand to completely cover your testicles, without squeezing them.

Place your left hand below your navel and rotate it over your skin. Feel the heat spreading through your abdominal region. Do 81 rotations (9 times 9, which is the supreme Yang number).

- Lightly contract the muscles surrounding your anus, without using your buttocks. To feel the contractions better, you can place a finger in your anus. Next, contract the muscles around the base of your penis. Placing one finger on either side of your penis will help you feel the contraction. Now alternate contractions of the sphincter muscle in the anus with those of the urogenital muscles around the base of the penis. Your fingers will tell you whether you are separating the muscle contractions properly or not.

- The last muscle to contract is the one which runs across your perineum. Place your index finger halfway between your scrotum and anus. Keep the other fingers on the base of your penis and in your anus, in order to verify whether you are contracting the perineum muscle separately.

The advantage of being able to contract the different muscles in the pubiococcygeal group separately is that it will enable you to fully control your orgasm reflex.

When you feel ejaculation is imminent, you can stop it by releasing the muscles around the scrotum and relaxing your buttocks. At the same time, you contract the muscles around the base of the penis to block the seminal passageway.

ADVANTAGES OF
THIS TECHNIQUE

You'll be amazed to find that such a simple technique can have such a powerful impact. Practice the stag exercise daily, and your entire sexual anatomy will be revitalised. The pubiococcygeal muscles form the basis of sexual potency, and this exercise will strengthen them considerably. The better shape they are in, the more powerful your orgasms will be, and the more rapidly you will regain your erections.

You'll also have more resistance to stress, due to the stimulation of the suprarenalis (adrenal) glands.

The muscular contractions involved in the stag exercise will strengthen your intestines, and aid digestion.

If you suffer from haemorrhoids, you will notice a rapid improvement due to the strengthening of the anal sphincter and the internal wall of the rectum.

By doing the stag exercise, you will become fully familiar with your pubiococcygeal muscle zone, and learn to control the various muscles before making love. Another important benefit of the exercise is that it strengthens the prostate gland. A strong prostate is essential for maintaining an erection and retarding ejaculation.

THE GREAT CONTRACTION

This is a very effective variation of the stag exercise: Clench your teeth, press your tongue against your palate, contract your pubiococcygeal muscles, tighten your fists as much as possible, and contract the muscles in your toes and feet; while doing this, inhale forcefully, imagining that your are pumping all your sexual energy upwards, towards your head.

After a complete contraction, relax all your muscles and breathe out slowly. Concentrate on your testicles and especially on your scrotum, in order to relax them completely. Remember that when the testicles are contracted into the body, ejaculation is imminent.

In time, you will be able to block the ejaculation reflex simply by clenching your fists and imagining that your sexual energy is flowing into your arms. The principle of retention is always the same: you have to decentralise genital tension and spread it through the rest of your body.

The Seventh Secret

◆

The smaller
heavenly cycle

ENERGY CIRCULATION
TECHNIQUES

We will now discuss one of the most important aspects
of the internal Taoist system. The ancient Chinese
developed a remarkable understanding of the human
body.

Through introspective analysis, they discovered how
vital energy accumulates in the organism. This vital
energy or *chi* circulates along precise channels, called

meridians. Acupuncture, which is becoming more and more familiar to Westerners, uses tiny needles to stimulate the flow of *chi* energy.

In their attempts to study acupuncture and verify its effectiveness, Western scientists have realised just how accurate the meridian system is. Lawrence Young, a New York medical doctor, wrote in 1983:

"I analysed recent electrophysiological studies on acupuncture meridians. These meridians do exist, in the sense that they are an electrophysiological phenomenon. In addition, the chart of points and meridians developed scientifically, shows that the traditional Chinese chart is 80 to 90 per cent accurate.

"Stimulating the appropriate acupuncture points results in real neuroendocrine secretions, and measurable physiological changes. These changes are discernible through electroencephalographic readings, exactly like the electric pulses emitted by the brain."

As children, we were always brimming with energy because there were no obstacles to the circulation of *chi* through the meridians. Unfortunately, as we grow older, we develop blocks in the system. This leads to fatigue, exhaustion, and eventually to illness. On the other hand, proper circulation of vital energy along the meridians results in good health and longevity.

This energy circulation is also of capital importance in the sexual act as perceived by Taoists. Firstly, it revitalises the libido in cases of impotence. Secondly, it aids in the redistribution of the libidinal energy which, when excessive, is a frequent cause of premature ejaculation.

OPENING THE ENERGY CENTRES

Improving energy circulation begins with the opening of the principle energy centres, through which the meridian channels pass. In the drawing on the next page, you can see where these different centres are located. The procedure for 'opening' the centres is as follows:

- First try to concentrate mentally on each centre.

- Visualise energy in the form of a spiral, moving through the various centres.

- Use a finger or an object (a pencil for example) to press on your skin above each energy centre.

The most important centre of all is the *hara*. If you only work on one energy centre, make it this one.

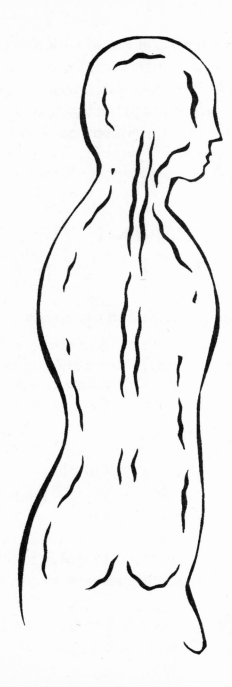

The *hara* is situated just below the navel, and is of capital importance in all martial arts. It is equally important in the art of lovemaking, in order to control ejaculation.

The *hara* is the vital centre of your entire being. For Orientals, it constitutes a second brain. Ideally, this, and not your head, is where you should localise your consciousness. And the *hara* is where you store up all your excess energy.

Imagine your meridian system as the road-map of a country. The capital city of this country is the *hara*, towards which all roads converge. The other energy centres are secondary cities, with some being more important than others.

The large stomach depicted in statues and drawings of the Chinese Buddha symbolises the power of the *hara*, centre and source of vital energy. To meditate on the *hara*, press a finger against your navel. Feel your breath as it fills and empties the area around the navel. Try to perceive the subtle energy concentrated in this area. In the same way as a foetus is nourished through the umbilical cord, you are nourished with universal *chi* energy through the *hara* centre.

OPENING OF
THE SMALLER
CELESTIAL CYCLE

Among the different energy circuits in the body, the smaller celestial cycle plays an essential role in regulating sexual energy.

The smaller celestial cycle begins and ends in the region around the navel – the *hara*. When the circuit is closed, vital energy (*chi*) circulates freely. Running through all the vital organs, *chi* fortifies the brain, maintains sexual potency, and invigorates the entire organism.

Two basic channels make up the smaller celestial cycle.

The **governing** channel is Yang. It starts at the navel, passes through the genitals, perineum and coccyx. From there it rises up the spine to the palate of the mouth.

The **functional** channel is Yin. It begins at the tip of the tongue, descends through the throat, solar plexus and stomach, and ends at the navel, where it joins up with the governing channel.

You can actually feel where the two channels link up by pressing the tip of your tongue against your palate.

Activating the smaller celestial cycle requires an effort of will-power at first, but in time it becomes automatic.

Once the process is begun, you will feel the benefits of a continual flow of vital energy through your system. This will result in better general health, and increased sexual potency, ample reward for the effort you are required to make.

METHOD

- Get comfortable in a seated position, with your back straight and your legs crossed (if possible). Close your mouth, and press the tip of your tongue against your palate. Do some deep, slow breathing, through your nose (if possible). Feel the *chi* energy accumulating in your *hara*, the area just below your navel. Taoists compare this centre to a furnace, where air is heated up.

- Visualise the energy revolving in a spiral around your navel. If you have trouble feeling the *chi*, use your hand to trace a spiral on the skin around your navel. Do this as long as is necessary for you to feel the vital energy in your abdominal furnace.

- Once you feel the energy, you can move on to the next step. Contract your sphincter muscles, and press your chin down against your chest. These two movements help direct energy from the navel to the genitals. Now concentrate on the movement of *chi* accumulated in the *hara* along the governing circuit. Vital energy first penetrates the genitals, then rises up the spine. Along the way, it energises the adrenal glands, pancreas, thymus, thyroid, and hypophysis (pituitary), situated at the base of the skull.

- Because your tongue is pressed against your palate, the *chi* energy now enters the functional circuit. Feel it descending down through your throat, chest and stomach, and back to the *hara*, where it joins up with the governing circuit. Synchronise the rotations of the cycle with your breathing. To end the exercise, always bring the energy back into the abdominal cavity.

- This is how the smaller celestial cycle works. Run through the circuit in your mind. You will know that you have really established the smaller cycle when you can feel the subtle energy flowing through the point where your tongue and palate meet.

A TECHNIQUE FOR BECOMING AWARE OF THE SMALLER CELESTIAL CYCLE

You can also use a form of Shiatsu massage to help activate the circuit. Here is how to proceed:

- Place the fingers of your right hand between your testicles and anus. Press hard. At the same time, place the tip of your tongue on your palate, and press hard. Try to feel the energy above and below, as you apply pressure.

- Now, starting between your legs, trace the path of the smaller celestial cycle (up your spine) using your fingers.

- When you reach the middle of your back, lift your left hand over your shoulder and try to join it to the right (if you cannot get your hands to actually touch, it doesn't matter). Continue tracing the path of the cycle with your left hand.

- Run your left hand up the back of your neck, over the skull, down the centre of your face, along your throat, chest, stomach and abdomen, until you reach the point where you started (between the testicles and anus).

- Now let your right hand take over once again. Repeat the cycle a number of times, going a little faster each time.

- As a variation, you can do the same exercise, starting with the left hand instead of the right.

- If you have trouble doing the exercise as described above, try it in the following manner: place both hands behind you so that they are touching between your legs. Run them up your back as far as you can. Then lift them over your shoulders and place them on your back. Continue tracing the path of the smaller celestial cycle in this way (over the head and down the front of the body).

- Whatever method you use, always terminate the exercise by pressing on your navel to stabilise the *chi* energy in that area. Meditate on this centre for as long as you like.

Freud was perfectly correct when he spoke about channelling sexual energy. However, what he thought was simply a metaphor is, for Taoists, a fact. According to Taoism, you must actively circulate sexual energy through well-defined channels, so that it revitalises other parts of the body.

Practising the smaller celestial cycle will make you more aware of your energy circuits, and allow you to redistribute accumulated energy. If you do not redistribute this energy, it will build up to a point where you have to expel it by ejaculating.

When you channel your sexual energy properly, you become, in terms of Chinese imagery, a winged dragon. Instead of weighing you down, your sexual energy will give you wings, which will in turn raise your consciousness, so that you acquire superior vision and understanding of the world in which you live.

The Eighth Secret

◆

Sperm Retention

AN ERRONEOUS CONCEPT OF SEXUAL PROWESS

Too often, men measure their sexual prowess by the number of times they are able to ejaculate when sleeping with a woman. The Taoist concept of sexual prowess is completely different. The less a man ejaculates, the greater his sexual prowess becomes. The more he learns to control the ejaculation reflex, the longer he will maintain his potency.

This principle is not completely unknown in the West. Rasputin was reputed to have practised it when making love with a number of women during the rituals of the Khlytis sect to which he belonged. This does not necessarily mean that he was 'debauched', in the ordinary sense of the word. Rasputin claimed he was like a piece of wood when making love with a woman. He must have practised a form of sexual retention, resembling that of the Taoists. And this is probably also how he developed his remarkable powers as a hypnotist, clairvoyant and miracle worker.

SEXUAL UNION AS ADVOCATED BY THE TAOISTS

Every era has had its sexual obsessions. It's simply a part of human nature. But here in the West, sexuality has been repressed for centuries. We are just now evolving out of a puritan attitude that was as ferocious as it was hypocritical. Moving from one extreme to another, we now see sex displayed almost everywhere we look. Advertising is inundated with shapely bodies in suggestive poses, selling anything from breakfast cereals to Venetian blinds.

In the face of this overwhelming solicitation, men tend to spend their sperm recklessly, without any measure of control. Ejaculation being one of the few natural pleasures left, men tend to abuse the privilege.

A Taoist text outlines the best path to follow:

"The instrument (penis) of a man who really understands Tao will not grow weak, even if he copulates with 100 women. He who has learned the Tao knows how to nourish his Yang from the Yin of his partner. He knows how to breathe correctly, and strengthen his essential forces. He knows how to retain his king (sperm), and refrain from ejaculating all night long. If a man understands Tao, he will have carnal relations with many more women, and feel better for it. But if he ignores the Tao, a single woman will send him to the grave."

Soen Sse-mo, a Taoist doctor of the sixth century, explained it this way:

"A man can enter into profound union with a woman without losing his king (sperm). A man who can make love without ejaculating will reach a very old age."

It is worthwhile noting that Soen Sse-mo lived to be 101 years old. Did he reach this venerable age by avoiding the company of women? On the contrary, he warned us about the dangers of a life deprived of the benefits of the union of Yin and Yang.

This ancient doctor recommended practising sexual union as often as possible. Reconciling this with the concept of sperm conservation is one of the most precious Taoist secrets.

But first let's look at how ancient Taoist intuition has recently been validated by modern science.

THE IMPORTANCE
OF SPERM

Taoists consider sperm to be an extremely precious and powerful substance. According to them, sperm is a concentration of vital and nutritious elements, which is psychically charged.

Modern science has proven them correct. Stephen Chang, a modern Taoist master, who holds degrees in both oriental and occidental medicine, states that: "Research has shown that the sperm emitted in one ejaculation has the equivalent nutritional value of two steaks, ten eggs, six oranges and two lemons." A highly reputed endocrinologist, Professor Sajaus, states that sperm contains the same hormones or internal secretions found in glands, including lecithin, phosphorus, calcium, iron and vitamin E. These elements all have great nutritional value, and play an important role in maintaining physiological balance.

The more often a man ejaculates, the more sperm his body must produce. A single ejaculation can contain up to 200 million spermatozoids, almost equivalent to the entire population of the United States! To replace all these living cells, the organism requires a great quantity of raw materials. The sexual glands extract these materials from the body, and perform successive refining operations on them. Excessive ejaculation, therefore, depletes the body of its raw materials. This results in physical and mental fatigue, and premature ageing. As Viktoras Kulvinskas states in his book *Survival Into The 21st Century*:

"Sperm loss is a contributing factor in all forms of illness. The chemical composition of sperm is similar to that of nerves and brain cells. These are the first organs to be affected. Since the body is completely dependent on the energy circulating through the nerves, sperm loss affects the entire body. [. . .] In addition, the loss of calcium and phosphorus through ejaculation is particularly high, and can affect the process of bone formation. When sperm loss was corrected through experiments conducted by Doctors Steinachan and Vornoff, all the symptoms of the various disorders disappeared; patients regained their vigour and seemed to grow younger . . ."

THE DANGERS OF CONTINENCE

Taoists recommend not wasting king, the precious male sperm. Conserving the essence of Yang fortifies a man and brings him closer to heaven. Does this mean that Taoists preach continence? Not at all. They have never advocated giving up sex, either to men or women. Complete abstinence is harmful, except in rare cases of individuals who have attained a high degree of spirituality. Suppressing sexuality does not remove desire, it simply forces it to express itself in unconscious ways, leading to a host of perversions.

The Catholic Church has had some experience in this area, since it imposes chastity on all its priests. And priests who do succeed in remaining chaste suffer from another problem – atrophy of the sex glands. Cancer of the prostate occurs more frequently among celibate priests than elsewhere in the male population.

Let's listen to what Soen Sso-mo (the sixth-century Taoist doctor quoted earlier, who lived to be 101 years old) has to say on the subject of continence:

"Without a woman, a man will not live to an old age. Without a man, a woman cannot be happy. If a man does not have a woman, he will not cease desiring one. This ardent desire will tire his mind. If his mind is tired, he cannot hope to attain longevity. Of course, if he really has no desire and no need for a woman, all the better. Such a man can live for a long time. But this type of person is extremely rare. If a man tries to suppress ejaculation for a period of time, he will have a lot of trouble conserving his king, and will lose it easily. He will ejaculate while sleeping or even pollute his urine. Or he will be haunted by succubi. Losing king in this way is a hundred times more harmful than ejaculating while making love."

THE MEANING OF 'RETURNING THE SPERM'

Sperm retention fortifies the entire organism. Taoists call this returning the sperm. Sperm ejaculated into the vagina of a woman can lead to the birth of a child. Such is its immense creative power. But a man who returns his sperm can regenerate himself.

The contractions performed during the stag exercise play a large part in returning the sperm. They create a pumping action on the prostate, which results in an influx of sperm. The sperm travels along certain passages, back to the testicles.

The contractions of the stag exercise also activate blood circulation in the testicles and in the region of the hips. This results in increased secretions by the testicles, which penetrate into the veins and circulate throughout the entire body. The vital substances contained in these secretions (male hormones, vitamins, etc.) nourish the glands and nerves. This leads to increased virility and vitality.

The Taoist idea that sperm retention is a cause of longevity has been confirmed by modern research. A. Bogomoletz states that:

"In a series of recent attempts at rejuvenating the organism, old age is considered to be an effect of insufficient internal glandular secretions and, in particular, the result of the extinction of the internal secretion functions of the sex glands."

CALCULATE THE FREQUENCY OF YOUR EJACULATIONS

To what point should sperm be conserved? Soen Sse-mo explains:

"When a man's king (sperm) diminishes, he falls ill. When king is exhausted, he dies. If he wants to live a long life and remain in good health, he must limit his emission of sperm. At 20 years old, he can ejaculate once every four days; at 30 years old, once every eight days; at 40 years old, once every 10 days; at 50 years old, once every 20 days. Past the age of 60, a man should stop ejaculating altogether. However, if he is exceptionally healthy and robust, he can continue to ejaculate once a month."

These numbers are relative, and do not constitute an absolute norm. How frequently can you ejaculate without abusing your system? The answer varies from individual to individual, and with age.

The contemporary Taoist master, Stephen Chang, developed an extremely useful technique which can give you a general idea of what your limit is. Divide your age by five and round off the number. This gives you the number of days you need to recuperate between ejaculations. For example, if a man is 34 years old, he would need seven days to recuperate. If he is in good health, he can ejaculate once a week. However, if he is ill or extremely weak, he should abstain from ejaculating and give his body a chance to accumulate vital energy.

CALCULATE YOUR BIO-ENERGETIC AGE

You can use this formula for calculating the frequency of ejaculation in a reverse sense, to estimate your bio-energetic age.

After ejaculating, do the following test: avoid all sexual stimulation for as many days as possible, and keep count of the days; when suppressed in this way, sexual pressure will accumulate; you will find yourself having more and more sexual fantasies and thinking erotic thoughts; when these become an obsession, and you feel you absolutely must have sex, note how many days have passed since your last ejaculation. Multiply this number by five, and you will have a precise idea of your bio-energetic age.

This can be very different from your real age. Take the example of a 53-year-old man who looks younger than his years. By doing the test, he will observe that after nine days of abstinence, sexual pressure becomes so intense that he can hardly control it. His bio-energetic age would therefore be about 45.

WHEN SHOULD YOU EJACULATE?

As it circulates through the smaller celestial cycle, sperm is recycled through the entire organism. In fact, Taoist methods are so effective, that even if you ejaculate after practising them, your body will have already extracted most of the essential vital elements from your sperm. The residue, which you lose during the occasional ejaculation, is not enough to endanger your health or exhaust you.

To be certain not to exhaust yourself by ejaculating, practice mutual absorption with your partner, in addition to the other exercises. Don't forget, your partner absorbs your Yang energy through your sperm. This is why Taoists affirm that all Yang energy lost through the sperm should be compensated for by the conscious absorption of an equivalent amount of Yin energy.

Absorbing Yin fluids is effected through the penis, if you can prolong penetration. You can also absorb Yin energy by sucking on your partner's breasts, which secrete a kind of psychic milk, rich in Yin nectar. Saliva and vaginal fluids also contain an extremely vitalising psychic essence which can be absorbed. Taoists call this drinking from the Jade Fountain.

Before ejaculating, take your bio-energetic age into account, as well as your physical and mental condition, and the weather outside. If you are sick, depressed or confused, or if the weather is too grey, too hot or too cold, it is preferable not to ejaculate. Also ask yourself the following question: "Will ejaculating lower my energy level, or lower our energy as a couple?" Above all, don't force yourself to ejaculate because your partner wants you to.

If you are faced with some important challenge, for example, if you are expecting to conclude an important financial transaction, or if you have to deal with people who are your enemies, it is advisable to conserve your sperm. Doing so will fill you with energy, courage and magnetism. During your partner's orgasm, invoke the power of her Yin energy to protect you and give you the strength of a celestial dragon.

With practice, you will know when to ejaculate. You will make the decision to ejaculate or not, spontaneously, and without regret.

CONVINCING YOUR PARTNER

A man who practises sperm retention may encounter an obstacle in his partner's resistance to the idea, even if she continues having orgasms. A woman may feel that a sexual encounter is not complete without ejaculation. There is not much awareness of Taoist principles here in the West, and women may find the idea of coitus without ejaculation somewhat surprising at first. Men should therefore explain what they are doing, and why, to their partners. Women will then understand that conserving vital energy does not mean they are loved any less.

To convince your partner, you can quote the following dialogue, taken from *Secret Prescriptions For The Bedroom*:

Question: "It is generally believed that men experience great pleasure when ejaculating. But when they learn about Tao, they ejaculate less and less. Does not their pleasure diminish because of this?"

Answer: "Absolutely not. After ejaculating, a man is tired. There is a ringing in his ears, his eyes grow heavy and he craves sleep. He is thirsty, and his limbs are inert and aching. He may experience a brief moment of joy while ejaculating, but this is followed by long hours of lassitude. If, on the other hand, a man controls his ejaculations and reduces their frequency to a minimum, his body will be fortified, his mind will be alert, his hearing and his vision will improve. And even though he restrains himself from experiencing the pleasure of ejaculation, his love for his partner will grow. It is as if he can never possess her enough. Is this not an infinitely more satisfying kind of pleasure for both the man and woman?"

LEARNING TO CONTROL EJACULATION

The best way to control ejaculation is to learn to determine your point of no return , that is to say, the point at which the ejaculation mechanism can no longer be controlled by will-power. You should determine this point by masturbating, and not while making love. Taoists have always taught this principle, which was rediscovered by Masters and Johnson. Here's how to proceed:

- Start masturbating. When you feel that ejaculation is imminent, stop for a while. Breathe deeply. The automatic spasms associated with ejaculation occur when breathing is shallow and the heart is beating rapidly. So take a few deep breaths.

- Now practice the stag exercise. Imagine that your sexual energy is rising up your spine, and flowing into your brain. Remember, your real sexual organ is your brain.

- Close your eyes and press your tongue to your palate. Breathe deeply, and visualise the following: your thorax is like a syringe; each inhalation raises your diaphragm, pushing your sexual energy upwards. You will soon feel the remarkable effects of this energy circulating in your body. If you feel a shivering sensation along your spine, you will know that your sexual energy has found the right path.

- Stimulate your sexual organs once again, taking care not to pass the threshold of ejaculation. In this way you can prolong your pleasure almost indefinitely. Don't forget that orgasms really happen in your brain, even if you ejaculate through your penis. The overall feeling of well-being you experience is more important than the ejaculation itself.

- One indication of imminent ejaculation is the position of the testicles. Before the crucial moment, they are pulled up against the base of the penis. It's a little like loading a gun. This positions the sperm channels for ejaculation. Watch out for this phenomenon. If it occurs, and you continue stimulating your genitals, ejaculation will follow automatically. So you have the choice of ejaculating, or pausing before continuing the stimulation. Ideally, you would learn to relax your urogenital muscles, as well as the muscular and fibrous sack which surrounds your testicles. This will enable you to exercise perfect and effortless control over your ejaculations.

• When you feel that ejaculation is inevitable, you can press on your perineum, using three fingers. Press with your index, third and ring fingers on the area between your testicles and anus. This pressure can block the spasmodic contractions which cause ejaculation. If you do ejaculate, pressure on the seminal passages can help retain the sperm in the channels, resulting in an interior ejaculation.

This technique is called the Chinese three-finger technique, so as to distinguish it from the technique suggested by Masters and Johnson, which consists of squeezing hard on the base of the penis, using the thumb and index finger. The advantage of the Chinese technique is that the penis does not have to be withdrawn from the vagina. The rhythm of your lovemaking is therefore not interrupted, which is the case with the Masters and Johnson technique.

To avoid ejaculating, you can also clench your fists very tightly, and then release them slowly. This serves to diffuse excess sexual energy to other parts of the body. Clenching the fists is even more effective when combined with the stag exercise. While clenching your fists, contract your PC (pubiococcygeal) muscles, which include all the muscles from the coccyx to the pelvis. Then open your fists slowly, while relaxing your PC.

To verify how effective these measures are, masturbate until you feel you are about to reach the point of no return. Then practice contracting your PC muscles and clenching your fists, until you feel your erection weaken. Start masturbating again until you are fully erect, then do the contractions to weaken your erection. Repeat the cycle at least three times.

If you ejaculate, try not to exceed your quota, as calculated in the previous section. If you don't ejaculate, you can masturbate as often as you like, without becoming in the least tired. You may feel some pressure in the area of the gonads, parochially referred to as 'blue balls'. Although slightly uncomfortable, this kind of tension is not at all dangerous, and the following section will explain how to get rid of it.

HOW TO DISSOLVE SEXUAL TENSIONS

Taoist practices can result in unaccustomed sexual tensions. Fortunately, the Taoists also developed methods for adapting to this more intense energy level. Here are some of the techniques:

• During and after masturbation sessions, do the Taoist exercises for circulating energy: the smaller celestial cycle, or better still the greater celestial cycle. This will relax the prostate gland and distribute the excess energy you have accumulated throughout your body.

• Vigorously massaging the knees with your fists has the same effect. A lot of sexual tension accumulates in the knees.

• A cold water sitz bath can have remarkable effects. Fill a bidet (or any large container) with cold water and immerse your genitals and anal region. Do this slowly, in a relaxed way. This will release sexual tensions. The technique can also be used before sexual relations to avoid premature ejaculation, whenever you feel overly excited.

• Sexual desire causes a contraction of the striated tissue surrounding the gonads. Grasp the skin of your scrotum, and pull as much as possible without hurting yourself. This will create a very pleasant, cool sensation.

- Practice the iron horseman exercise. Stand up, with your back straight, and your feet spread well apart. Bend your knees a little, remembering to keep your back straight. Imagine that you are sitting on a horse, with your feet in the stirrups. Pull on the reins by throwing your shoulders back a little, then place your hands on your thighs, palms facing upward. Maintain the position for five minutes, as immobile as a statue. This is a classic martial arts exercise. It helps strengthen the entire *hara* region, and develops your vital male energy. It also helps control ejaculation, and intensifies sexual pleasure.

The Ninth Secret

◆

Riding the wave of desire

THE TECHNIQUE OF VALLEY ORGASM

Here in the West, coitus often resembles a flash-fire, characterised by a brief period of chaotic activity, followed by complete exhaustion. Taoists view the sexual act quite differently: it should unfold like a dance or a session of Tai Chi, in harmonious rhythm. Relations can also take place in almost total immobility. Here, it is the internal movement of Yin and Yang energy which

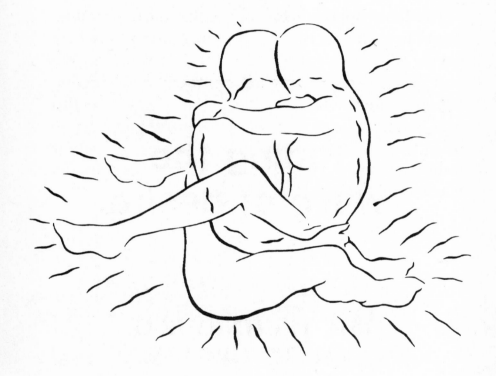

gives the act its dynamic quality. These internal movements are the same as those described in the section on the smaller celestial cycle.

The Taoist approach transforms sex into real meditation. The principle is one of forming a single circle of energy with your partner. Genital contact of the Yin and Yang creates electromagnetic energy which revitalises the couple. One advantage of making love in this way is that it helps control ejaculation. You have to learn to tame your desire, that is to say, to become familiar with its power without trying to escape by ejaculating too quickly.

HOW TO TAME DESIRE THROUGH IMMOBILE COITUS

- Reduce your movements to a minimum. Don't move at all, unless you feel you will lose your erection. Then, a few gentle movements of the penis will consolidate your erection so that you can continue making love. The sitting and lateral positions are especially favourable for this exercise.

- Both of you should concentrate on your breathing. Feel yourselves breathing together, in harmony, perfectly synchronised. Ideally, you would both breathe at exactly the same rhythm. If you are both attentive, you will be amazed at how effortlessly your breathing fuses into one. We strongly recommend practising breathing exercises alone before trying this meditation.

- Press the tip of your tongue against that of your partner. This closes the circuit, and together you establish the smaller celestial cycle. When you practice the cycle alone, you close the circuit by pressing your tongue against your palate. The energy circuit starts at the perineum, rises up the spine to your skull, and descends through the tongue down to the abdomen. During coitus, you and your partner fuse your smaller celestial cycles into one.

The tips of your tongues form the junction between your two internal energy cycles. Take care not to move your tongue too much. Instead, try to feel the current of electrical energy passing from one tongue to the other. If your tongue starts quivering on its own, then you know that contact has been established. It may even happen that the energy between you becomes too intense, at which point you simply break the connection for a short time.

Concentrate on the complete energy circuit link-
ing you together. When you practice the smaller
celestial cycle as a couple, the energy does not des-
cend down to the abdomen, but flows into the other
person through the tongue. It then flows down your
partner's spinal cord, passes between her buttocks
and enters her genitals. You will be sure to feel a hot
current circulating between your genitals and
your partner's.

- From time to time, do the stag exercise to circulate
  your energy, or to stop yourself from ejaculating.
  Imagine that the muscular contractions are pumping energy upwards.

- Remember that the aim here is not genital orgasm,
  but prolonged and intensely pleasurable union.
  Close your eyes. Feel your partner's body, her heat,
  her energy flowing into you. Let yourself melt in
  the current of heat, completely fusing with her.
  Slowly, your breathing will become synchronised,
  until you are both breathing as one person. This
  deep and silent communion with another person
  will create a marvellous sense of fulfilment. You
  will feel complete, in harmony with nature, at
  peace with the entire universe. Forget about your
  troubles, about society and all its masks and false
  morals. Shut off your internal computer, suspend

your thoughts for a while, and exist in the perfect bliss of the here and now.

A MORE ADVANCED METHOD: THE EMBRACE OF FIRE

Remaining immobile during coitus is an ideal way of discovering the non-genital dimension of sexuality. It is also very helpful in learning to control the ejaculation reflex. When you feel you have fully mastered this step, you can move on to the embrace of fire. Here you alternate a passive phase with an active phase.

The first thing you do is to heighten erotic tension to its maximum through passionate embrace. Move as much as you like. Do some PC contractions to make sure you can control your excitement. Stimulate your partner in any way you choose. Slow down at certain moments, then increase the pleasure level some more.

When either you or your partner reach the point of orgasm, stop. Practice the contraction exercises. Slow your breathing down. Get into a comfortable position, and begin a period of immobility.

After a certain time, you can resume the active phase again. Return to the embrace of fire. Then, when you feel the need to continue once more, stop. Fuse your energy with that of your partner.

You will experience valley orgasm when your mind is completely empty, that is to say, at the moment when all thoughts have left your mind, including the desire to ejaculate. You will resemble a surfer, carried along on the wave of your partner's pleasure. Even the highest wave cannot throw you off balance. From this point on, you feel as comfortable in the active phase as in the passive.

The secret lies in being relaxed and natural, completely concentrated on the present moment. In fact, valley orgasm (or implosive orgasm) is not something you can attain by trying, as is the case with ordinary orgasm. It occurs when you least expect it to happen. It's a little like being suddenly inspired with a great idea.

Physical tension associated with the experience of pleasure diminishes, and is replaced by very subtle sensations of ecstasy and pleasure. Now sex becomes a doorway to something greater and more fundamental – Tao, the Cosmos – which represents a significant jump in your level of consciousness. This is the path of valley orgasm.

MORE TECHNIQUES FOR PRACTISING RETENTION AND INTENSIFYING PLEASURE

The basic principle of sperm retention is to prevent sexual energy from remaining localised in the genitals. We have already described a number of techniques which are helpful for controlling ejaculation. Here are a few more:

- After a long sea voyage, Chinese sailors would masturbate before going to visit a prostitute. This prevented them from ejaculating too quickly, and not getting their money's worth. If you are just beginning your Taoist practice, this simple technique can work for you as well.

- Press on the acupuncture point called *Ping-I* situated three centimetres above the right nipple.

- When you feel you are close to ejaculating, clench your teeth as much as possible. Press your eyes shut. Listen for a sound or vibration between your ears.

- Visualise a spiral at the level of your forehead. Alternate nine revolutions in a clockwise direction with nine revolutions in a counter-clockwise direction. Keep concentrating on the spiral for as long as it takes to reduce sexual tension.

- Roll you eyes around in both directions (this may worry your partner a little, so explain what you're doing and why!). This will draw the energy up into your eyes, and result in great clarity of mind.

- Visualise the energy of your sperm rising in a spiral around the spinal cord, right up to the top of your head. Then bring the energy back down to your navel. Stabilise it there by visualising nine concentric spirals over this area.

- Visualise a golden serpent rising up your back to your skull, and then descending back down to the stomach, where it swallows its own tail. Imagine it turning round faster and faster. Then slow it down.

- Visualise your desire as a sun the size of an orange in the area of your pubis. See your desire as pure energy, like fire. Then bring this sun up to the level of your navel. Now you feel an incredible force overwhelming your entire being. You can also visualise the sun between your breasts, and imagine it radiating gentle, beneficial heat, which gradually spreads through your chest and into the rest of your body.

- You can also practice visualising the 32 parts of the body. This is a technique which is more Buddhist than Taoist. Decompose the exterior image of your partner's body while successively perceiving the following 32 elements: hair, body hair, nails, teeth, skin, muscles, tendons, bones, marrow, kidneys, heart, liver, serous membrane, mesentery, pancreas, bladder, lungs, stomach, excrement, brain, bile, digestive sugars, pus, blood, oil, fat, tears, sweat, saliva, mucus, urine, and fluid in the joints.

  You can also try visualising these 32 elements in yourself. Get as deep as possible into your own body, as if you were exploring a marvellous cave. Take a trip through your circulatory or nervous system. Try to feel the most subtle exchanges of energy taking place in your body.

- The opposite of separating your partner into minute parts is to visualise her as a golden goddess, wearing fabulous jewels and a crown. Visualise her angelic aspect. Try to perceive her aura, and her subtle astral body.

- Also, try to perceive the animal deity or totem which corresponds to your partner's personality. Remember the Egyptian gods, half human, half animal. The principle here is similar. Each of us has a particular animalistic aspect in addition to being human. Some women evoke the tranquil power of a tigress or lioness. Others suggest the grace of a swan or gazelle. Try to perceive this slightly mysterious animal power in your partner. This will make your contact with her less genital and more energised.

• As a parallel to the preceding technique, visualise the process of transformation of sexual energy *(tsing)* into vital energy *(chi)*. Imagine sexual energy radiating from the lower abdomen, and flowing through the energy circuits of your partner's body. Imagine the contractions of the stag exercise pumping your own sexual energy upwards, nourishing your organs and psychic centres on its path. If a part of your body is sick, imagine the sexual energy flowing into that area, healing and revitalising it.

• Don't forget to use the Chinese three-finger technique. When ejaculation seems imminent, stop all your movements and, if you have time, pull out of your partner's vagina. Press firmly on the point situated midway between the anus and testicles. This is the area which produces the contractions which precede ejaculation. By applying pressure, you stop the contractions. Don't start moving in the vagina again until you have regained full control.

• Many men tend to become extremely serious when making love. This is a mistake, since it only serves to increase anxiety about performance.

   Try to see the humorous side of things, and laugh at yourself a little. Start with your eyes. Relax them, while visualising yourself smiling radiantly. The eyes are directly related to the central nervous system. Once they are relaxed, your whole body will feel the warmth you are radiating. Let the energy of love and laughter spread through your body, especially into your heart and abdomen. This technique can also be used to prevent premature ejaculation and to overcome impotence, and will also heighten sexual pleasure.

• Imagine a ball of golden nectar at the top of your head. Visualise it turning into liquid and spreading through your body. Feel the smooth revitalising liquid flowing into every part of your body.

RIDING THE WAVE OF DESIRE

The principle of effective sperm retention is to approach ejaculation without crossing the threshold, beyond which ejaculation occurs automatically.

A skilled lover can detect when he is approaching his threshold. The heart beats more rapidly, breathing accelerates, the testicles are retracted up against the base of the penis, and the buttocks become tight. At this point, all stimulation must be interrupted. If you feel very close to the point of no return, withdraw your penis completely.

The stag exercise is a very effective way of preventing the prostate from setting off the spasmodic contractions associated with ejaculation. The advanced practitioner can control ejaculation with this technique alone.

The Taoist principle is really very simple. By approaching your threshold without going beyond it, you can prolong the intense pleasure that would normally lead to ejaculation indefinitely. Of course, this is a little like walking a tightrope or climbing a steep mountain. You need to be very vigilant in order not to fall, but the pleasure experienced at these heights is well worth the effort!

With practice, you will eventually have the following revelation: orgasmic spasms without ejaculation! You'll be very surprised the first time it happens. The feeling is just as pleasurable and soothing as if you had really ejaculated. You may ask yourself what happened to your sperm! This is the miracle of Taoist sexual transformation, which occurs when you are least expecting it, and without effort.

You will experience the absolute height of sexual pleasure, while coming out a winner as far as vital energy is concerned, since your *tsing* (sexual energy) is accumulated instead of lost, and transformed into *chi* (vital energy). In this way, a man becomes charged with magnetism and vitality.

THE DIFFERENCE BETWEEN TAOIST RETENTION AND COITUS RESERVATUS

The two techniques are very different despite their apparent similarities. In coitus reservatus, men retain their sperm in order to avoid impregnating their partner. The idea is actually absurd, since the lubricating liquid secreted during sexual contact can contain sperm. When practised too often, coitus reservatus has two major drawbacks: sexual tension accumulates and can affect your moods and general state of mind; the practice can also lead to chronic prostate problems.

The Taoist technique of retention does not create such problems, since it allows you to recycle sexual energy by distributing it through your entire body. In comparison, coitus reservatus (also called coitus interruptus) is more a form of repression than actual retention.

In the Taoist art of loving, you will discover the ultimate pleasure of desiring without desire. The duality between desire and the fulfilment of desire will no longer exist. Desire becomes fulfilment, and is replaced by the powerful, extremely intense energy of pure love.

In Taoist texts, we often encounter the expression 'riding the wave of ecstasy'. Allow us to draw a parallel between the art of loving and the equestrian art: the power of desire can be compared to a horse; an in-experienced rider will practice with a gentle, well-trained horse; he will first walk, and then move up to a trot. This corresponds to the first two stages of valley orgasm, where you alternate immobility with the embrace of fire.

A skilled rider will want a faster, more spirited horse. If he has a lot of experience, he will be able to break in young horses, and even tame wild horses. This is the height of the equestrian art. At this stage, your knowledge and skill are beyond any specific techniques. Your partner may use all her charms, but you will remain concentrated and imperturbable.

Now you are able to ride the most powerful wave of desire without fear. This absence of fear on your part is essential. Your partner will feel secure. She won't have to worry about whether or not you're going to ejaculate before she attains satisfaction. She won't be afraid of exciting you too much, and will thus be able to abandon herself completely to the spontaneous experience of sexual ecstasy.

The more you learn to 'stay in the saddle', that is to say, not ejaculate, the higher the level of energy and ecstasy you will be able to attain. A time will come when unimaginable forces are released inside you. You will experience an intensity which goes far beyond what you have experienced during ordinary copulation, and discover what is most savage and free in yourself.

Both on the physical and mental level, you and your partner will transcend the limits of the ordinary self. Time will cease as you enter the dimension of eternity. You will no longer be human beings making love, but gods ... two divinities joined into one ... two persons forming a single god, experiencing the mystery of the holy duality of Yin and Yang.

It's all a question of practice. Never let yourself get discouraged. And remember that even the most experienced rider sometimes falls off!

The Tenth Secret

◆

Benefits of
meditation

Making love in the present moment is not easy in this
tumultuous day and age, obsessed as we are with speed
and instant gratification. This is why meditation is so
important.

Lao Tsu defined meditation as follows:

"Let your mind think whatever it wants."

Meditation does not mean stopping all thinking, but
observing what you think. The ultimate goal of medita-

tion is to know your inner self. This means understanding how you think, feel, breathe, etc. Meditation is a kind of absolute intimacy with yourself. In solitude, you can drop the masks of your thoughts and feelings.

But to do so, you must allow your mind to think whatever it wants. Let your thoughts arise as they will, whether good or bad. Don't judge them. Don't identify your true self with them. Observe how they arise and interfere with your actions. In this way, you will perceive the subtle mechanism of the mind, and understand how you are playing hide and seek with yourself.

When you meditate, you should be as coldly objective as a scientist bent over a microscope. However, this should not exclude a certain sense of marvel. As Pasteur said, looking through a microscope was his way of relaxing and forgetting about his cares.

Pasteur's way of getting totally absorbed in his work closely resembles meditation. The only difference is that during meditation, it is the turmoil of your own mind that you observe, instead of a culture in a glass dish. Meditation is a state of self-absorption, coupled with self-observation.

However, this descent into yourself has nothing to do with contemplating your own navel. When you meditate, your perspective should resemble that of an astronomer, studying the distant stars. By creating a distance between yourself and your problems, you can resolve them. Your third eye is the lens of both a microscope and a telescope. It allows you to simultaneously see things which are very close as if they were very far away.

HOW DOES MEDITATION AFFECT YOUR SEXUAL LIFE?

Meditation is definitely the supreme therapy. One of the first effects of meditation is that it relaxes you, but this is not the ultimate goal. Meditation helps you get into harmony with yourself, your sexuality, and your partner. It allows you to discover the causes of your problems, whether sexual or otherwise. Couples who meditate together can overcome crisis situations much more easily. Meditating alone or with your partner, before making love, will make the experience very different. You'll be much more tuned in to your sensations and feelings, and have more confidence in yourself and in your partner.

HOW TO MEDITATE

Sit on a chair or on the ground. If you use a chair, be sure to keep your back straight, and don't lean against the back of the chair. Plant your two feet on the ground. You can also sit cross-legged (or half crossed if this is too difficult) on the floor (preferably on a carpet, with a pillow under your buttocks to help keep your back straight).

Meditation almost always starts with breathing. We have already explained, in the section on the Fifth Secret, how to breath correctly. Now you should try to observe the relation between the play of your thoughts and your breathing. It's not easy to reach a state where you are a pure observer of your thoughts.

If you get into a debate in your mind, your awareness will become cloudy, and your mind will wander. Lao Tsu said: "Let the troubled waters settle, and soon your mind becomes clear." The more agitated you are when you begin, the longer it will take to attain a state of objective clarity.

Keep your mind inactive, but at the same time do not try to suppress your thoughts. Just observe them as they arise. Concentrate on your breathing. By remaining immobile in the centre of your being, the mud in your mind will gradually sink into your unconscious, leaving your conscious mind clear.

During meditation, your thoughts will eventually stop flowing on their own, as you distance yourself from them through self-observation.

When you have attained a satisfactory degree of mental calm, you can enter a deeper state of meditation. Take a voyage through the interior of your own body. While concentrating on your breathing, you will explore all the centres and energy channels in your body (see the Seventh Secret).

MEDITATING ON THE ELEMENTS

To gain a better understanding of your sexual energy, it is very useful to learn to meditate on the elements.

In Taoist philosophy, all manifestations of universal energy result from the interaction of five basic elements: fire, earth, metal, water, and wood. This is similar to Western esoteric philosophy, which uses four elements: air, water, fire, and earth.

As far as sexuality is concerned, meditating on fire and water are most important. Water is the symbol for women, fire for men. During sexual relations, men must economise on their supply of wood – sperm – to feed their fire. This is the only way men can heat up their partner.

On the other hand, men can learn to use the water in themselves to calm the fire when it burns too intensely. Understanding the interaction between water and fire is essential for mastering sexual energy.

FIRE MEDITATION

Meditating on fire means re-establishing contact with the essence of your masculinity. You can simply sit in front of a camp-fire or fireplace and meditate on the flames. Ideally, you would do this when you are alone, and out in nature. There is nothing depressing about solitude. On the contrary, it will revitalise you.

You can meditate on fire at any time. For example, observe the flame when you light up a gas stove or a candle. Even cigarettes would be a good object of meditation, if they didn't have the negative side-effects (as you may know, tobacco is considered a ritual substance by North American Indians – the transformation of tobacco into smoke symbolises the transformation of gross matter into a more subtle, spiritual dimension).

When you meditate on fire, identify yourself with the various stages of combustion. Feel as if you are the wood, the coals, the fire itself, the ashes and the smoke. Meditating on fire is actually meditating on the process of internal combustion, as the slag of your mind is burned away. Your mind becomes a furnace where you can burn up harmful thoughts and emotions.

Meditating on the outer or inner fire purifies your being of everything that is useless or artificial.

Look at the diagram on page 88. You will see how fire is associated with the major energy centres. For Taoists, true alchemy consists of the internal work of transforming sexual energy.

FIRE VISUALISATION

Here are some visualisations which may help you perceive the fire in yourself:

• Concentrate on the centre of your feet. Imagine a current of orange fire energy entering both your feet and running up your legs. It passes through your sexual organs, right up to your heart. From there it moves down into your hands. Feel the power of the fire in your hands.

- If you are sexually aroused, concentrate on your sexual organs. Visualise your arousal as fire, which first warms your heart, and then spreads to the rest of your body.

- Visualise a burning sun in a limpid sky. Sense the heat from the sun descending progressively into all parts of your body.

- If you are very aroused, visualise your sexual centre as a ball of fire. As you breathe in, imagine your legs are a well, in which cool, blue water, is slowly rising. Let the water fill your abdomen, and feel it cooling the fire down. As you breathe out, direct the cooling water to other parts of your body. Imagine yourself becoming totally refreshed and calm.

WATER MEDITATION

In the *Tao Te King*, Lao Tsu wrote a vibrant eulogy on the subject of water:

"Water benefits everything and harms nothing. It resides in the depths, out of the reach of men. It is very close to Tao."

Water infiltrates everywhere and takes any form. It is totally supple and adapts to any container into which it is poured. With perfect humility, it never seeks to elevate itself, unless the element of fire brings it to a boil. Water teaches you to flow, to get around all obstacles. In its infinite patience, it can overwhelm the highest cliff.

Whether pure or polluted, whether in the form of vapour or ice, snow or rain, water remains water. But despite its apparent simplicity, science still considers water one of the most mysterious elements in nature.

MEDITATING ON WATER IS ACTUALLY MEDITATING ON THE PROFOUND NATURE OF WOMEN

To meditate on water, start by observing it in its day-to-day functions, for example, when you fill a saucepan or a cup. Watch water boiling on the stove and transforming into vapour. Go and sit by a river or lake, or by the ocean. Watch the torrents of water flowing from rock to rock, or the waves breaking against the shore. As you identify yourself with water in all its stages of transformation, you will see how it corresponds to your various states of mind. Don't forget that your own body is composed of 75 per cent water! Become aware of all the water inside you. Whenever you take a bath, become one with the water you are immersed in.

WATER VISUALISATION

Here are three visualisations which will help you feel the water inside yourself:

- Visualise a desert in the area of your throat. The sky is very blue, the sun burning hot. Once the vision is clear, breathe out very slowly, imagining that your breath is a current of very blue water, flowing across the desert.

- When you have mastered this step, start imagining that each time you exhale, this current of water divides into a number of tributaries. As you inhale, visualise grass and flowers growing in the desert.

- As you breathe in, visualise a spring of cool, very blue water, rising up through your legs until it reaches the top of your skull. As you breathe out, visualise the water bubbling upwards from the top of your head. See the water splashing all around you. As you breathe in, suck up all the water, and then make it bubble over again as you breathe out. Imagine that you are a fountain standing in the middle of a pond.

The Eleventh Secret

◆

The food
of love

DON'T EAT
TOO MUCH

Taoists recommend that you never fill your stomach to capacity. When the stomach is two-thirds full, digestion takes place without your even noticing it. But persons who eat too much, feel heavy and sleepy. Their ability to concentrate is affected. If men try to make love in this state, they may not be able to get an erection, or if they do, they will probably ejaculate too quickly.

Taoist masters also advise against making love right after eating, even if you had a light meal. If you eat a lot, all the more reason to abstain from sex!

EAT IN PEACE

Taoists insist on the importance of always being in a calm frame of mind when you eat. If you are troubled, preoccupied, tense, and so on, you will digest badly. Your organism has an immense alchemical task to perform every time you eat, transforming the raw materials contained in food into energy.

Whatever the quality of the food you eat, it will weigh heavily on your internal organs if you are in a state of emotional stress. So try to eat in peace! If you are not alone at the table, try to create a harmonious ambiance. Avoid disputes during meals – this is not the time to settle arguments or enter into conflicts.

Don't eat in haste, while watching television or thinking about other things. Always chew your food well. It will taste better, and make the task of digestion much easier. Concentrate only on the food you are absorbing.

Take fruit, for example – fruit is not just a piece of merchandise, but concentrated solar energy that has been prepared for you by nature – it is a love-letter from the Tao. A feeling of gratitude would not be inappropriate. Follow the example of Jesus, who made each meal a celebration!

If you chew your food well, you will savour its nutritional ingredients and feel fully satisfied. You won't want to overeat. Obesity is one of the plagues of our consumer society, and causes all kinds of physical and mental disease.

THE TAOIST CONCEPTION OF FOOD

Should Taoists avoid eating meat altogether?

There is no Taoist dogma concerning vegetarianism. Abstaining from meat is not, in itself, an assurance of greater spirituality. Remember that Adolph Hitler was a strict vegetarian! Every person must determine what is best for his or her own spiritual development. If you know how to listen to your body, it will tell you what to eat and what to avoid.

However, be careful about overindulging your taste buds. Sugar, fat, fried and processed foods may taste good, but what your body really needs is fresh, clean food. Fruits and vegetables, and juices made from them, are irreplaceable.

Generally speaking, cooking destroys a large part of the enzymes, vitamins and minerals contained in food. This is especially true the longer your food is cooked, and the higher the cooking temperature is. Canned foods are not recommended. The best way to cook your vegetables and grains is to steam them, since they lose less of their essential nutrients.

FOODS RECOMMENDED FOR INCREASING SEXUAL VITALITY

Nuts and grains

Nuts are a fantastic concentration of vegetable matter. An entire tree and all its nutrients are contained in each nut. They are, therefore, extremely rich in nutrients, as are grains like sunflower seeds, sesame seeds, and so on. The proteins found in nuts and grains help vegetarians do without meat.

Grains and nuts are also good for the immune system, the prostate, and the production of sperm cells. Don't roast them, if you want to get the maximum benefit from the enzymes and vitamins they contain. Vegetable oils are also easier to digest if they are not cooked.

Sesame seeds are particularly rich in vitamin E, which is the vitamin most associated with sexuality. Tahini (butter made from sesame seeds) and halvah (a mixture of sesame and honey) can increase virility.

Eggs and milk

Try to eat fertilised eggs, which are produced from the union of cock and hen, and which contain all the elements necessary for the hatching of a future chick. When you eat a fertilised egg, you are the direct beneficiary of all this potential energy. The proteins concentrated in such eggs will maintain your sexual potency. You're better off not eating more then three eggs per week, to avoid building up cholesterol in your blood-vessels.

As for milk, it is the product of sexually mature cows, rich enough to feed calves, and therefore a very complete source of protein, both as milk and in its various forms of cheese, cream, yogurt, and so on.

Soya and tofu

Soya is a plant that has been known to the Chinese for thousands of years. It first appeared in Europe only 300 years ago. The United States is now the largest producer of soya in the world, with 65 per cent of all soya grown there.

Soya is a fantastic source of protein, containing 38 per cent protides. It is also full of phosphorus, iron, magnesium, chlorine, copper, potassium, sodium, sulphur and zinc. Phosphorus aids in cerebral activity, and in balancing the nervous system. Soya is also rich in vitamins E, A, B, and C. It contains non-saturated fatty acids, while animal fats are saturated. You can therefore eat soya without worrying about developing high blood pressure or arteriosclerosis.

Soya is energising, rich in minerals, and also contains lecithin, which helps circulate lipids to the liver. Unfortunately, despite all these advantages, soya is used in the West mainly to feed cattle!

Oriental cooking makes abundant use of soya. Miso is a paste made of fermented soya beans. Tamari is soya sauce. Soya oil is delicious on raw vegetable salads. Fortunately, people in the West are beginning to wake up to the nutritional value of soya.

Vegetarians love it as tofu, a preparation which resembles meat in its consistency, and which is extremely rich in proteins and minerals.

Seaweed

All life originates in the sea. Seaweed plays an essential role in the planet's food chain. Through photosynthesis, seaweed accumulates a vital and precious source of energy directly from the sun. Seaweed contains numerous vitamins, amino acids, glucides, lipids, protides, and practically no fat.

Seaweed also extracts an extraordinary number of minerals from the ocean, many of them in the form of trace elements. Proportionally speaking, seaweed contains more vitamins and minerals than any other food.

Scientists discovered that seaweed possesses antibiotic properties, and can also prevent tumours. People who are macrobiotic rave about the stimulating, revitalising, disintoxicating, strengthening and balancing effects of seaweed, which can be eaten raw, cooked in soup, used as a spice, or in delicious marine salads.

Food as aphrodisiacs

Certain foods are reputed to be aphrodisiacs. Garlic and onions both stimulate sexual functions. Avocado, asparagus, artichokes, celery, carrot juice, olive oil, wheat germ, dates, bananas and mangoes also have a positive effect on sexuality, not to mention meat, and seafoods like oysters, caviar, and various crustaceans.

Among the vitamins and minerals, the most important as far as sexuality is concerned, are vitamins E, C, B12, lecithin, zinc and selenium. However, vitamin E is by far the most important. Dietitians praise its anti-oxidising power, which helps cells remain young and strong, as well as its power as a sexual stimulant. Vitamin E has been successfully used to cure numerous cases of impotence and sterility.

Ginger

Ginger root helps blood circulation and, as you know, a man's capacity to get an erection is directly related to the circulation of blood. Ginger is not an aphrodisiac in the proper sense of the word, but it is an anti-stress and anti-asthenic food. It stimulates appetite and digestion.

When absorbed in large quantities, fresh ginger has a sudative effect (it causes perspiration). Try drinking an infusion of ginger sweetened with honey, and you will feel immediately invigorated.

Ginseng

Ginseng has always been thought to have aphrodisiacal properties. And in China, it has also always been associated with longevity. What exactly is ginseng?

Studies conducted in Russia have shown that ginseng can cure impotence. In other experiments, ginseng favoured the development of sexual organs in young mice. These reached puberty more rapidly, and developed a prostate gland which was 40 to 60 per cent larger than normal.

However, ginseng is not an aphrodisiac, properly speaking. It does not cause an erection. In France, experiments have been carried out with a substance called papaverine. Men suffering from chronic impotence were given an injection of papaverine, which caused them to become erect, and remain so for at least an hour. So while papaverine can be called a true aphrodisiac, ginseng cannot.

It would be more precise to define it as an adaptogene, as the Russian researcher Brekhman called it. He remarked that the effect of ginseng on the body is nonspecific. Ginseng stimulates the entire organism, and reinforces the body's immune system. It therefore does have an effect on sexual function, which depends on the body's overall condition of health and vitality. However, unlike papaverine, its effect on sexuality is not instantaneous, but progressive.

As for its reputation as a fountain of youth, this can also be explained by its capacity to fortify the immune system.

It was the custom in China to offer ginseng to elderly persons as a birthday present. It was a way of telling them they were loved, since ginseng helped prolong their lives. Even today, the elite class in China consumes very costly wild ginseng root (a single such root can cost thousands of US dollars!). Mao Tse-tung himself regularly used ginseng.

In Europe, gerontologists are turning more and more to ginseng, notably to improve concentration and memory, and to combat depression and premature senility. Unfortunately, there is no controlled study which confirms the fact that ginseng actually prolongs life. However, it has been proven to improve the quality of life in elderly people.

To paraphrase the slogan of the *American Gerontological Society*: "Ginseng adds life to your years instead of years to your life."

Numerous studies have confirmed the positive effects of ginseng. Here are a few of their findings:

- Ginseng improves intellectual and physical performance.

- It increases endurance during extended periods of intense effort.

- It regularises sexual functions and can combat infertility.

- It eases arterial tension (lowering it when it is too high, and raising it when it is too low).

HOW TO CONSUME GINSENG

- The best way is to use the actual root. Don't skimp on price. Inferior quality ginseng (better than nothing!) is found in various liquid and powdered preparations.

- If you buy red Korean ginseng root, ask for sky quality, one of the best on the market. Also, try to find out how old the root was when picked – it should be at least seven years old.

- What is called Siberian ginseng is actually a plant of the same family, *eleutherus*. Its effects are very similar to those of real ginseng.

- If you do a ginseng cure, take 1,000 to 3,000 milligrams per day to make sure you get results. After a few days, diminish your intake.

- The Chinese often serve ginseng with two other plants, which balance its effect. Men take it with Foo-Tsi-Tseng and Gotukola (available in most Chinese pharmacies); women should take it with angelica and liquorice.

The Twelfth Secret

◆

A place to
make love

FENG SHUI

Since antiquity, the Chinese have always constructed
their habitations in accordance with the principles of
Feng Shui. Today, Chinese people all over the world
still apply the same principles. Even some skyscrapers,
built by Chinese entrepreneurs, conform to the Feng
Shui system.

The Feng Shui philosophy of architecture believes
that a badly designed, incorrectly positioned building
can engender illness and premature death in its

occupants. In terms of business, it can lead to eventual bankruptcy, although a modern architect may see nothing wrong with the construction.

This antique science has been reborn in a movement called geobiology. Geobiological architecture is also referred to as the 'medicine of habitation'.

The ancient Chinese understood the importance of magnetic currents. We now know that the presence of an underground river, for example, can have a serious effect on health.

The first to scientifically prove this phenomenon was Baron G. V. von Pohl, in Germany in 1929. He found an abnormally high rate of cancer in one southern German town, and noticed that 54 patients who died in a one year period lived above an underground river. Other sudies have confirmed his findings.

The Chinese considered things like the influence of the landscape, the position of trees, the proximity of water, or establishments like slaughter houses or cemeteries, in their design of human habitations. They would give advice to builders: no rocks or trees in front of the main doorway, for example, as these would inhibit the flow of energy; very windy spots should be avoided, as they result in a dispersion of energy. Fortunately, Feng Shui consultants were able to rectify mistakes, notably by positioning mirrors!

The purpose of this book is not to introduce you to the complex art of Feng Shui. Suffice it to say that Feng Shui principles are being adapted by modern architects, in their search for better, more liveable dwellings. A number of books have already been published on the subject, in case you want more information on how Feng Shui can improve your sexual life.

The important thing to remember is that if the space in which you live is badly designed, it can become a cause of many health problems, including sexual or conjugal difficulties.

WHAT CONSTITUTES A HEALTHY HOUSE?

In light of recent studies, here are some things you should look out for:

- Living or working in proximity to high tension wires can have serious consequences: cancer, leukaemia, stress, irritation, and so on. You also have to be careful with the electromagnetic radiation emitted by household appliances, especially in your bedroom. A television or computer will disturb the balance of ions in the room, which might lead to insomnia or nightmares. It is even better not to have an electric plug or even a radio next to your bed.

- Living in high-rise buildings also has certain harmful consequences. Steel girders encased in concrete create what is known as the Faraday's cage effect, which cuts off the magnetic forces of the earth, as well as cosmic currents. Don't be surprised if you live in a high-rise apartment building and often feel fatigued.

- Certain construction materials can also affect your health. Oil paints and synthetic carpets release gases whose effects are still unknown. The same goes for cleaners and pesticides.

HOW TO MAKE YOUR BEDROOM A REVITALISING AND BENEFICIAL SPACE FOR YOUR LOVE LIFE

According to Feng Shui, the bedroom is the most important room in the house. The quality of your sleep, sexuality, and general health depends on its design.

Even your professional life (and therefore your bank account) will suffer if the design of your bedroom disturbs your sleep.

Here are some principles that should be respected:

- Remember what we said earlier about electrical pollution. To maintain proper ion balance in your bedroom, air it out regularly, even in winter. Proper ion balance also requires sunlight. The sun emits powerful magnetic rays which energise the entire atmosphere in a room. They also eliminate psychic pollution and harmful astral influences.

  So make sure your room gets as much light as possible during the day. Ideally, the sun should shine in when you wake up in the morning. Open your curtains as soon as you get up.

- Feng Shui also recommends filling empty corners with plants, which will give your room maximum vitality. Being surrounded by plants is particularly beneficial for sexual relations, since you are more in contact with the magnetic forces of the earth.

- Get rid of negative images (photographs, paintings, and so on) from your walls. Many people surround themselves with art, but are unaware of the insidious effect these images have on their sub-conscious minds. These can be particularly harmful in the bedroom. What you see just before falling asleep can have a profound effect on your dreams. And while you sleep, you become much more vulnerable to impressions.

- Be careful about displaying famous works of art, whose aesthetic value is incontestable, but which depict morbid subjects. Rather, you should place photographs and prints of scenes which lead to positive associations, like a tropical sunset, or a beautiful rain-swept landscape. Also, pictures of great sages like the Buddha can help elevate the level of vibrations in your room.

- The colours of the space in which you live are also very important, and influence your state of mind. Avoid striped carpets, and heavy, oppressing colours or wallpaper, and so on.

- As for the placement of the bed, make sure it is not right next to a door. You should be able to see out through the door, even if it's only half open. This will make you feel secure, and recharge your room with energy from the rest of the house.

In general, the best orientation for a bed is facing north. But the other directions can also have positive effects, depending on the individual. Try out various directions, and see what works for you.

- Above all, avoid water-beds and electric blankets. Nothing has a more damaging effect on the biomagnetic field. On the other hand, there are magnetised beds that can vastly increase the vital energy circulating in your bedroom (they are very fashionable in Japan).

GENERAL ADVICE
FOR SLEEPING
BETTER

During sleep, your body recharges its batteries. The Feng Shui principles are especially concerned with improving the quality of sleep.

- Sleeping on the left side is not recommended. In this position, the lungs apply pressure on the heart. Sleeping on your right side, which places your heart above your liver, is much better. Sleeping on your stomach is also not recommended, since it inhibits breathing. You're much better off on your back. Keep your arms beside your body, and if it's not too cold, open a window. Take a few deep breaths, expelling all your cares as you exhale. Relax, and forget about your problems until tomorrow.

- Sleep is the best counsel, as the saying goes. Be attentive to your dreams. Try to remember them as soon as you wake up, as they usually fade quickly. Of course, many dreams won't make any sense, but those you find striking, usually carry some message from your subconscious. When you have a recurring dream, it means you are ignoring the message.

- Sleeping too much makes the body lazy and weak, and leads to all kinds of problems. Seven or eight hours of sleep per day is enough for most adults. If you practice Taoist yoga or meditation, you will be able to recuperate even more quickly – four or five hours of sleep will be sufficient. Meditate before going to sleep, and when you wake up. This will improve the quality of your sleep, revitalising you more rapidly, making it easier to wake up, and giving you more energy throughout the day. In fact, one hour of meditation is worth a few hours of sleep.

hope of finding the cause of premature ejaculation. They believe it is better to go directly to the real cause, that is to say, your energy level at the present moment.

From a Taoist point of view, premature ejaculation is essentially linked to a weakness in your energy system. There is a hole somewhere, and energy is escaping. In the case of premature ejaculation, this loss is effected by the emission of sperm. This is also the case for persons who have frequent wet dreams.

A Taoist therapist will therefore teach you techniques for harmonising your mind and nervous system, and how to lead a balanced life in terms of diet, proper breathing, and so on.

CAN MEN WHO ARE IMPOTENT PRACTISE TAO?

Taoism is essentially a discipline which awakens latent energy. By accumulating vital energy or *chi*, and calming your mind through meditation, a man approaches the consciousness of Tao. Powerful currents of energy arise and activate the psychic centres, after which a man can attain levels of power and superior consciousness. In his book on Aikido, M. di Villadorata cites some examples of the awakening of *chi* in day-to-day life:

"The clenched fist of a child that cannot be opened, or an arm that is so tensed up it cannot be bent against the child's will."

"The persuasive power of a salesman who succeeds in selling you something you don't really want or need."

"The magnetism of a political leader who can move a crowd to tears or fury."

"The strength of a mental patient during an attack of hysteria."

"A woman who is able to lift a car off the ground in order to save her child."

Western therapists do not seem to treat the cause of sexual impotence directly. Once again, Taoists consider impotence to be the consequence of a deficiency in *chi* energy. In fact, sexual energy is derived from this universal, vital energy, called *chi*.

However, don't start to worry if you sometimes feel an ebb in your sexual potency. This is not surprising, considering our modern lifestyle, so full of stress, and so distant from nature. Fortunately, by applying Taoist principles of nutrition, breathing and physical exercises, you can still accumulate *chi*, no matter where you live.

All you have to know is how to capture this pure energy, which is everywhere in the universe. When you are loaded with *chi* energy, everything becomes possible. Fear disappears, obstacles vanish. Therefore, it is by working directly on *chi* that you can solve all your problems, be they sexual or not. This is the simplest solution, even if your impotence appears to be more organic than psychological.

However, you should consult a doctor to know exactly what is going on. If surgery is necessary, go ahead with it. But you should also be doing Taoist exercises, so that you will progress more rapidly towards a complete cure.

If you get nocturnal erections, you can be sure you are not suffering from organic impotence.

For most Western men, getting an erection is a reflex phenomenon, over which they exercise little control. Younger men generally have no trouble becoming erect. On the other hand, their burning ardour tends not to last very long.

Older men do develop some measure of control, but often lose their vigour. Erections are not as hard, or are more slow in coming, and sometimes become the object of severe anxiety.

Western men are subject to so much stress they often have trouble maintaining an erection, which they may lose even before ejaculating themselves. Obviously, this is not very pleasant for the man or his partner. Many lovers resign themselves to the sad facts, thinking there is nothing they can do, that age is the only cause of the problem.

Taoists do not see it that way. They have discovered that the phenomenon of erection can be controlled, so that a man can build his ardour and attain a level of constancy that goes far beyond the usual degree of male potency. Their great secret is sexual transmutation.

THE TAOIST VIEW OF ALCHEMY, EROTICISM AND LONGEVITY

Although we have already touched on the term of sexual transmutation in this book, the expression takes on a very precise meaning in Taoist texts.

People in the West are familiar with the word alchemy. In popular imagery, an alchemist is someone who transforms base metals (lead, mercury, tin, and so on) into gold. There is some truth to this, but real alchemy is much more than that. Ultimately, alchemy is a process of spiritual transformation, based on the way matter reacts.

China also had its alchemists, and many of them were Taoists. Some of you may be surprised to know that in China, alchemy and eroticism went hand in hand. We can even talk about sexual alchemy, also called internal alchemy. In addition, this sexual alchemy was linked to the cult of longevity.

In internal alchemy, sperm becomes the object of the process of transmutation. It is the lead or mercury which must be transformed into gold. The abdomen is the furnace where this transformation takes place. As for desire, it is the alchemical fire, stoked by the breath of life.

In the alchemical process, heavy, lunar matter (sperm) takes on an extremely subtle, solar form.

These ideas may sound a little strange or vague, but they do have some very practical results. When sexual energy *(tsing)* is properly channelled and transmuted, it can vastly increase your store of vital energy *(chi)*. Your increased level of *chi* will engender a very special kind of energy which few people possess, called *chen*. *Chen* is spiritual and psychic energy combined, and gives rise to the so-called 'New Man'. Such a being can access powers and states of consciousness which are out of the ordinary. In addition, the interaction of *tsing, chi* and *chen* helps maintain sexual vitality to a ripe old age. And there lies one of the greatest revelations of Taoist practice!

We've had our sexual revolution here in the West, but centuries of repression cannot be erased that easily. This is why we find it normal, or at least not unusual, for persons past a certain age to lose all desire.

Some people, of course, have defied this belief, among them a number of celebrities. Victor Hugo, for example, was able to keep his young mistress satisfied at the age of 80. Picasso fathered a child in his seventies. Henry Miller led a remarkably active sexual life well into old age. However, none of these can equal the prowess demonstrated by an obscure French writer living in the eighteenth century who, allegedly lived to be 119 and who, at the age of 102, married a woman of 26, who bore him a number of children.

The sexual revolution has made us re-examine our attitudes towards sex. Unfortunately, most Westerners are still unaware of the high-tech sexual techniques developed by Taoists. The accumulation of vital energy, and the joy of living in the way of Tao, maintains health and prevents ageing. The path to astonishing longevity lies before you, and by this we mean longevity on all levels – physical, intellectual and sexual.

We are on firmer ground when we talk about the practical results of this system of thought, which in theory may seem a little strange. Of course, you cannot obtain results without doing a little work on yourself. Perseverance and discipline are essential. The Old Man must die before the alchemical process (work on the self) can give birth to the New Man lying dormant inside you.

You can't just press a button and expect the light to go on in your mind and body. Your entire energy system may be in very bad shape. You first have to repair and renew it. The energy system we are referring to is composed of energy meridians (see the Seventh Secret) which you can align and harmonise by practising the art of Taoist eroticism. This will gradually enable your psychic and subtle energy to circulate freely once again.

And then, everything will be possible.

On all levels.

Conclusion

We've talked a lot about technique in this book. But don't let that mislead you. Ultimately, perfection in the Taoist art of loving is attained when you forget about technique and learn to flow with the tide of loving energy.

The celebrated flautist, Jean-Pierre Rampal, once explained in an interview that he exercised vigorously before every concert. He studied and repeated each bar until he attained a degree of perfection that he found acceptable. However, during the actual concert, he took the risk of concentrating uniquely on the soul of the piece, and forced himself to forget about technique while he played.

This creative spontaneity is very different from what we call instinct, which most often engenders mechanical and repetitive behaviour. As far as sex is concerned, instinct is more likely to result in hasty encounters and premature ejaculation. We just have to look at the instinctive sexual behaviour of our primate ancestors. In fact, the aim of instinctive sexual behaviour is not pleasure or ecstasy, but simple reproduction. A number of researchers have asserted that Mother Nature favours rapid ejaculation in order to increase the chances of conception. Therefore, human beings have to restrain their instincts in order to develop new ways of enlarging the scope of their sexual experience. This is precisely what Taoist techniques aim to do.

However, an awareness of technique should not lead to an obsession with performance. All these erotic strategies only exist to give men the confidence and physical control necessary to open themselves to the amorous dimension of copulation. They can then explore the infinite possibilities which arise from the union of Yin and Yang, and fully satisfy their partner, both on a sexual and emotional level.